Viz
THE
PORKY CHOPPER

A meaty selection of prime, beefy, lean comic cuts from Viz issues 48 to 52. With stuffing. And sausages

Featuring material first published in Viz magazine between June 1991 and April 1992

Written, drawn and thrown together by
Chris Donald (Editor)
Graham Dury, Simon Thorp
and Simon Donald

With sizeable contributions from
Davey Jones and John Fardell.

Photography by Colin Davison.

OLD ROPE BOOKS

AN IMPRINT OF
JOHN BROWN PUBLISHING LIMITED

ISBN 1 870 870 336

Published in Great Britain. by John Brown Publishing Ltd.
The Boathouse, Crabtree Lane, Fulham, London SW6 8NJ.

First printing September 1993.

INTRODUCTION

Those of you old enough to remember the early nineties will no doubt smile with fond recollection at the mention of fold-away ironing boards, CD players, jug kettles, Jason Donovan and Kentucky Fried Chicken. Those of us fortunate enough to have been there during 1991 and 1992 will never forget those two most memorable years, and the lasting impression that the events of that particular 24 month period had on our lives.

But for many of us one memory lingers, outshining all others. And that is the golden memory of the halcyon days when Viz magazine used to be funny.

For today's car thieving, flammable track suit wearing, computer illiterate younger generation of ignoramuses, it is hard to believe that Viz used to be funny. But funny it was, and never more so than during the latter half of 1991 and the first four months of 1992. These were heady days for Britain's rudest magazine. The magazine where 'fuck' was a four letter word, and 'knob cheese' was two words, one of four letters, and one of six. The magazine that sold more than a million copies every issue, a familiar sight on newstands, newsagents' shelves, newsagents' counters and in increasingly large piles on newsagents' floors all over Britain. The expletive hungry magazine buying public were snapping up rude words, like 'beef curtains', faster than Viz could think them up. Along with milk men, Radio Three's Test Match Special and Broadmoor, Viz had become an institution.

But times were changing. French and British engineers shook hands through the newly constructed Channel Tunnel. Down came the Berlin Wall. The Milk Cup was replaced by the Coca Cola Cup, and the Government announced plans to widen the M25 motorway to four carriageways in both directions. These were times of rapid development, and like dinosaurs, steam trains and red telephone boxes before them, Viz was struggling to maintain the pace.

For those of us old enough to remember those good old days this book is a nostalgic walk down memory lane, to a time when Fat Slags said "Mess on me snatch" and the whole nation laughed in unison. To younger readers more familiar with computer games and solvent abuse, it will hopefully prove that there was a time when Viz was actually as funny as it used to be.

Whatever your age, whatever your disposition, I hope you will enjoy reading this book as much as the creators and publisher will enjoy spending the seven odd quid you paid for it. And I hope it conjures up as many fond memories of late 1991 and early 1992 for you as it has done for me.

Finally, this volume is especially dedicated to Mark E. Smith out of The Fall who, during an interview in 1986, became the first man in history to point out that Viz was no longer as funny as it used to be.

Professor Humphrey Arseholes, F.R.A.,
Reader in Adult Comics and Jazzmags,
Keeble College, Oxford.

August 1993

Wonderful Welsh heritage

I think it's wonderful that the Welsh have a language all of their own. It gives them a sense of identity and enables them to keep in touch with their roots.

It also means that us normal people don't have to talk to them.

A. Stapleton
Walthamstow

What do YOU think of the Welsh? Do you think they're alright? Or do you think they're bloody awful. Perhaps you think they sing to much, and that Max Boyce is a twat. Whatever you think, whether it's about the Welsh, or anyone else for that matter, write and let us know at our usual 'Letterbox' address.

There's a packet of biscuits for the sender of the best letter. Probably.

Footwear incentive

Footwear shop managers often give staff discounts on shoes. Would they not find it easier to recruit staff if they also gave similar discounts on inner soles, pop sox and odoureaters? I should be most interested to know what other readers think on this subject.

Tracey Arkell
Hindhead, Surrey

The horn seems to be the most under-used of all car accessories. I like to beep mine in time to a catchy tune on the radio, or occasionally make up my own tunes, much to the amusement of pedestrians. Perhaps other readers have interesting or novel uses for their car horns which they'd like to share.

R. Borrocks
Stockport

It makes me laugh when people say 'an Englishman's home is his castle'. I live in a one bedroomed council flat in Ripon. Then again I'm Welsh.

Rhys Thomas
Ripon

A castle yesterday.

They say 'a watched pot never boils'. What nonsense. I filled a pot with water and watched it boil in exactly 4 minutes 35 seconds.

Ian Goodall
Camden

They say the best way to a man's heart is through his stomach. That's absolute nonsense, and I should know. I am a heart surgeon, and the method I use is to make an incision in the thorassic cavity, bypass the myocardium, and once inside the rib cage its a simple matter of removing the pericardium, and hey presto! There it is.

Dr David Williams
Standish

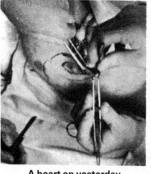

A heart op yesterday.

I decided to try this new form of smash and grab robbery they call 'ram raiding', and drove to a local off license, ploughing the car in through the shop window before making off with liquor and cigarettes. I thought my raid had been a success when I totted up my haul later – over £1000's worth of stolen goods. But the next day I got a bill from the garage for the damage to my car – it cost £1800 just to have it repaired!

I think I'll stick to conventional burglaries in future.

A. Smith
Gateshead

Summer is here again

With the approach of summer it is worth remembering that the playing of radios at high volume, especially in your garden, can annoy next door neighbours. Another good way is to set fire to their dustbin.

A. Gamble
Ormskirk

Dear Unity,

The other day I went to the Zoo. I'd had a few drinks and just didn't seem to care. The next thing I knew an elephant was undressing me. I knew it was wrong, but I just laid back and let it happen. The next thing I knew the elephant was making love to me, while several monkeys and a zebra caressed my naked body.

Now I feel so ashamed. What should I do?

Worried
Cheltenham

I am having a new fridge freezer delivered on Friday the 14th, and would appreciate it if motorists would avoid parking around the bottom of my drive as this space will be required for access.

Mr A. Swinton
22 Langley Park Gdns.
East Whitstead
Staffordshire

P.S. Motorists wishing to find alternative parking space in the vicinity may park on the yard opposite, at the back of the church, as long as they don't block the vicarage entrance.

LetterBocks
Viz Commick
P.O. Box 1 PT
Newcasle upon Tyne
NE99 1PT

IT'S 'FILEY' MINOGUE

Pint sized Aussie songstress Kylie Minogue has just splashed out a fortune on a new luxury home. But the sumptuous million pound holiday home is not in Beverley Hills, Bel Air or Barbados. It's in Filey.

The millionaire songbird has splashed out a cool £75 per week to rent the six-berth mobile home for a month on a static caravan park near Primrose Valley, Filey.

Kylie's dream home boasts:
* **Flushing** toilets
* **Twelve volt** electricity
* **Hot and cold** running water.
* 'Put-me-up' sofa beds, with accommodation for Kylie and up to five members of her Aussie entourage.

FACILITIES

As a guest at the caravan site, Kylie will be entitled to use facilities which include a camper's shop, á launderette, table tennis room, amusement arcade and fully licenced social club. And Fred Baxter, owner of the 2½ acre 'Sandy View' Caravan Park, has made an open invitation to Kylie to pop into one of their lively 'Come as you please' evenings, where holiday-makers provide their own entertainment, singing songs accompanied by Mrs Baxter on the organ, and her son David on drums.

EXCLUSIVE

Artists impressions of Kylie's dream home (right) and of the star sunbathing topless yesterday.

"I suppose Kylie will probably sing a medley of her hits, such as 'I Should Be So Lucky', 'The Locomotion', 'Je Ne Sais Pas Pourquoi' and 'Too Many Broken Hearts'. And although I can't guarantee it, there's no reason why Kylie shouldn't take advantage of our sunny East coast weather and go topless around the caravan site", said Mr Baxter.

CARAVANS

According to Mr Baxter any fans of Kylie's who wish to meet their favourite star are in luck. For there are many caravans, ranging from 2 to 8 berths, still available through the season.

EXCURSIONS

"I can't say exactly when Kylie will be here, but she'll be coming and going all summer, I'd imagine. No doubt she'll be using the park as a base from which to plan day trips and excursions throughout the Filey area".

FRIENDS

Many show biz friends of the Aussie star are expected to pop by from time to time, including Jason Donovan, Mick Hucknell out of INXS and Madge Ramsay.

DENIED

However, a spokesman for the Australian star last night denied Mr Baxter's claims. "To the best of our knowledge Kylie has no intention of visiting Filey at all this year", we were told. But Mr Baxter was unmmoved. "Kylie did mention that this holiday was going to be top secret. She obviously wants to get away from the pressures of show business, and hasn't told her management.

REQUEST

At Kylie's request I've tried to keep the whole thing under my hat, otherwise once she starts walking around her with her knockers on full show the press will be buzzing around here like flies round shit".

SPECTACLE wearers. Enjoy foreign language films without the bothersome sub-titles by sticking a strip of brown parcel tape across the lower half of your lenses.
**J. Lofts
Chiswick**

IMPRESS the girls this summer by driving up and down the seafront with an ironing board strapped to the roof of your car whilst playing Beach Boys music loudly on your cassette player.
**B. Meredith
Swansea**

STICKING two large black circles in the top corners of your TV screen makes the newsreaders look like Mickey Mouse.
**S. Teardrop
Teddlebranbuds**

HOUSEWIVES. When nipping to the shops always carry a stiff broom in the boot of your car. Use it to sweep the broken glass to the side of the road every time you have a minor accident.
**D. Stammers
Canvey Island**

* Do you have any amusing Top Tips or funny letters that you'd like our readers to share? Then why not send them to us at the 'Letterbox' address at the top of the page. Alternatively, you could just start your own 'adult' comic and stick them in that, together with a few rude cartoons about dog turds or similar, call it 'Arse' and publish it yourself. Which is what most people seem to be doing these days.

7

I'M ALIVE!

By JIM MORRISON

EXCLUSIVE

Sixties raver is living in Redditch

Morrison (above) as we saw him in the sixties and (right) with girlfriend Pamela Courson. (Left) Jim as he is today.

Sixties pop idol Jim Morrison, believed to have been dead since 1971, is ALIVE and well, and living in Redditch.

That is the stunning news set to rock the pop world to its foundations as a new film 'The Doors' smashes box office records across Britain and the USA.

The Hollywood blockbuster movie, starring Billy Idol as cult hero Morrison, is a steamy no-holds-barred sex romp depicting the drug crazed hippy lifestyle of the tragic sixties star. And as movie goers queue to see the film, record buyers are forking out a fortune on a re-released Doors album, plus the movie soundtrack LP.

MOVIE

But one man who is far from happy with the band's new found success is Jim Morrison himself. For the man on whom the movie is based won't earn a penny from the film, or booming record sales. In fact, Jim Morrison wasn't even invited to the premiere.

GINGER

"That really hurt", Jim told us yesterday, now a chubby looking 32-year-old, his hair an unfamiliar ginger. But beneath the spectacles, Morrison's penetrating eyes are unmistakable. "As far as the movie makers are concerned, I'm dead".

BOURBON

Morrison's alleged 'death' twenty years ago has always been shrouded in mystery and the subject of speculation. The official verdict was that he died of a heart attack in his Paris hotel bathroom in 1971. "That was all a big mix-up", he claims.

"I'd been having sex and had taken a few drugs and decided to have a bath. I must have been really tired because I dozed off. While I was asleep a reporter who was in the room asked a friend if I was alright. 'He's dead *tired*', she told him. Of course, the reporter missed the last word, and mistakenly took it that I was dead".

DIGESTIVE

The next day all the papers announced Morrison's death. "Once they get hold of a story like that there's not really a lot you can do about it", he told us.

FIG ROLL

Morrison returned to England and lay low for several months, eventually re-surfacing in Redditch where he took up a job as a stationery salesman with his uncle's firm. "I was fed up with the music business, so I decided to start a new career".

COMPANY

Now, many years on, Morrison runs the company, supplying anything from paper clips to staple removers, doing brisk business with firms throughout the Redditch area. but occasionally Jim yearns for the rock 'n' roll lifestyle he left behind, and the new film has served to remind him of the good times he had.

"I must admit, I did go to see the movie", he confesses, a surprisingly short, rounded figure, dressed in a smart suit and tie. "To be honest I was disappointed. There wasn't enough sex, drink or drugs in it. It all looked tame compared to some of the things I used to get up to".

His face broadens into a nostalgic smile as he recalls those crazy days of the sixties. "It was just one big party. A non-stop sex marathon, with a never ending diet of booze, drugs and groupies".

OPTIONS

"There's one occasion I'll never forget. I was high on drugs and having sex with a groupy backstage. Suddenly the curtain went up and there was the audience – ten thousand people – all watching yours truly getting stuck in! They loved it! In fact, it wasn't long before everyone was joining in, and

soon the entire crowd had stripped off and were giving it six nowt with each other".

COSMOPOLITAN

Morrison sits back and smiles as the memories come flooding back. "I was having sex non-stop, 24 hours a day for weeks on end. So much so that if I ever stopped for some reason, it used to take about a day for my arse to stop going up and down".

HOUSE BEAUTIFUL

"And of course drugs were all the rage in those days. Real drugs, not the rubbish they have today. One day I'd been experimenting with LSD. I drank about ten pints of the stuff, poured a bit up my nose, put a few drops in my eyes, and then shoved the rest up my arse."

GOLDFISH

"It was fantastic! What a trip that was. I can't remember anything else that happened until I woke up six months later in Paul McCartney's goldfish pond having sex with Twiggy, Keith Richards and a dolphin".

PARROT

Jim claims the original idea for The Doors film was his. "I wrote the script over three months ago and sent it to Hollywood, but I heard

'My Paris hotel bath death tragedy was all a big mix-up'

nothing. The next thing I know the film was released. It's got to be more than just coincidence. If only I'd kept a copy of that script".

HENDRY

Unfortunately Jim doesn't have the financial backing required to fight his case in the courts. "I lost my passport, and my birth certificate was ruined in a washing machine, so legally its impossible for me to prove my identity". But Jim is fighting back, and now he is planning his own film which he claims will tell the **TRUE** story about The Doors.

WERBENUIK

Work on the new movie 'Come On Baby Light My Fire' is due to start soon in a garage adjoining Jim's business premises in Redditch. And according to Morrison, Hollywood superstar Burt Reynolds has expressed an interest in the role of the singer.

And a revealing new book which Jim claims will blow the lid off the swinging sixties is also planned.

Burt Reynolds yesterday.

"We're talking about the most controversial book ever published", said Jim yesterday. "Not only does it name all the top society birds I shagged, but it also names all the birds everyone else shagged. The Beatles, The Stones, everyone. And there's even pictures of us all doing it, by John Lennon, and some red hot photos by Lord Snowdon". The book, due to be released simultaneously with the movie, will be called 'Try To Set The Night On *Fye-yerrr*', and should be ready for a winter release.

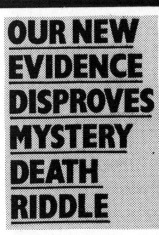

OUR NEW EVIDENCE DISPROVES MYSTERY DEATH RIDDLE

Record company chiefs, film makers and even solicitors representing Morrison's estate refused to believe us when we told them that Jim was still alive. And they say that our man Jim Morrison is a **FAKE.**

ARSEHOLES

But our own investigations have cast serious doubts over the so-called 'death' of the star in 1971, and we believe the new evidence speaks for itself.

★The only person who is supposed to have seen Jim Morrison dead in his bath was his girlfriend Pamela Courson. *Three years later Pamela Courson died mysteriously,* after taking a fatal drugs overdose.

★When somebody dies, the police usually draw around their body with chalk. But to our knowledge *no chalk lines were found in the bathroom where Morrison is alleged to have died.*

★When we rang the French police to ask if a file on the Morrison 'death' was available, a foreign speaking buffoon pretended not to understand us, then promptly *hung up.*

★Despite hours of searching in a Paris cemetery, we were unable to find any gravestone bearing the name Morrison.

POP SAYS 'NO' TO NOOSE

Darling Buds of May star David Jason, who plays Pop Larkin in the smash hit comedy series, will be the last in line for the job of hangman should the Government vote to re-introduce capital punishment.

PERFICK

For the veteran comedy actor, who also starred as 'plonker' Rodney in Only Fools And Horses, is strongly opposed to the death sentence. And a showbiz insider has revealed that Jason, 63, is the last man prison officials should choose to carry out the sentences. "It's really a specialised job, and I can't see that David, with his acting background, would be at all qualified, far less willing to do that sort of thing", we were told.

PLONKER

In fact, if the black cap were to return, and executions were to re-commence in Britains gaols, officials may have to look beyond the cast of the hit TV series to find their new Official Executioner. For the word in showbiz circles is that other members of the cast would also turn their noses up at the post.

We rang actress Catherine Zeta Jones, who plays Mariette in the series, because she's the one everybody fancies. But she wasn't in.

11

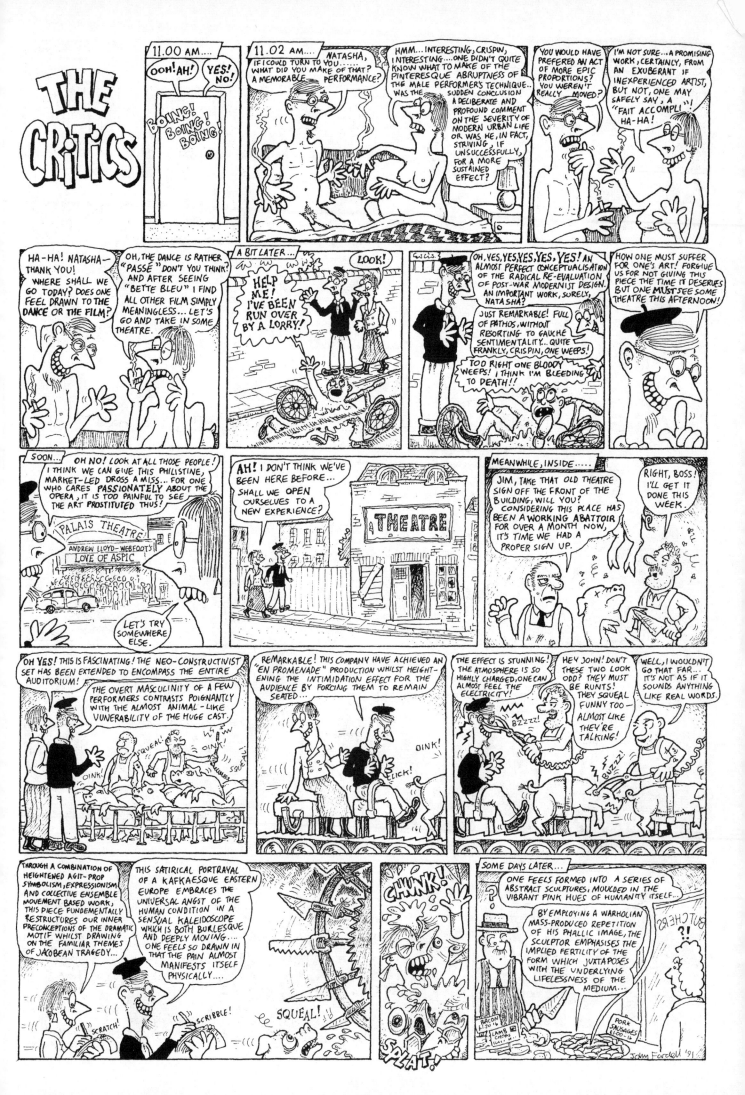

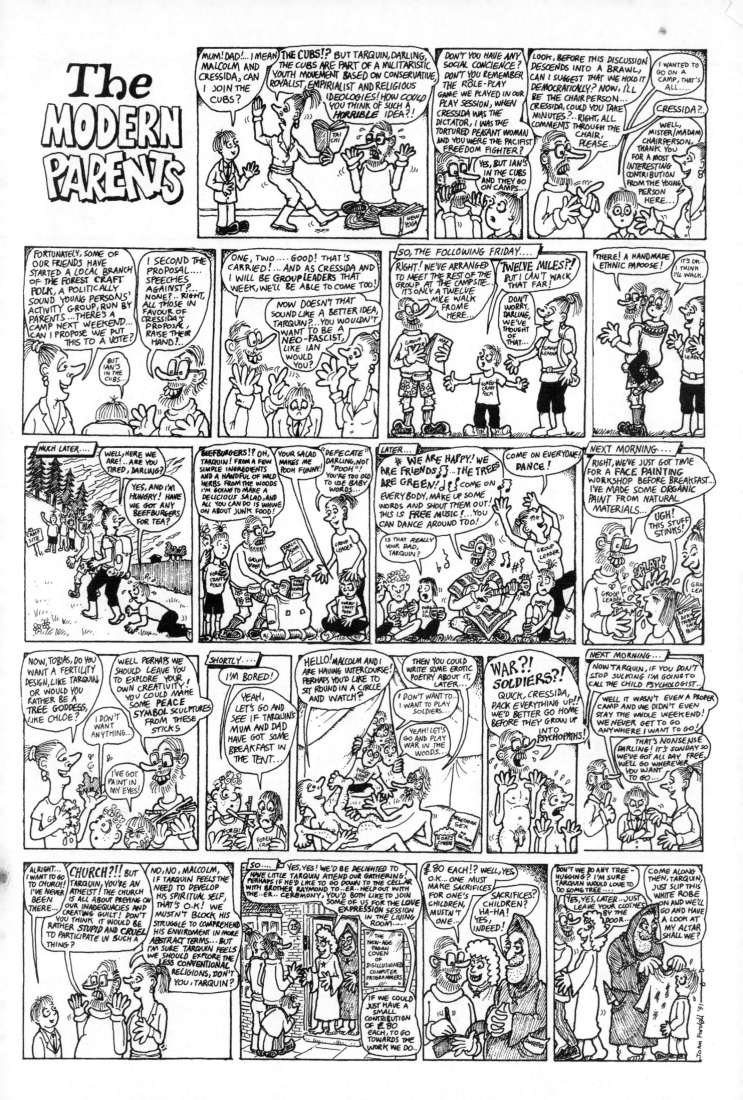

POP IN THE YEAR 2000

First came Elvis – with his tight trousers. Then came the Fab Four, with mop top hair cuts and electric guitars. Then there was the Bay City Rollers, with tartan patches and stack heeled boots.

And now we've got Kylie, with her great big teeth and tiny tits. Yes, the face of pop music is ever changing. Stars rise and fall in the winking of an eye, as the pop roller coaster trundles ever onwards. As well as changing fashions, new technology greatly influences the music scene. '78's were replaced by singles, then singles gave way to '45's. Cassettes replaced albums, and now LPs have given way to the 'CD'.

INSIGHT

So what can the pop pickers of tomorrow expect to listen to? And what kind of stars will be Top of the Pops in the 21st century? Here's a fascinating insight into the amazing space age world of pop in the year 2000.

In the year 2000, the world's top pop event, the Eurovision Song Contest, will be a thing of the past. Instead, space viewers from all over the Universe will tune in on their satellite TVs to watch the Galactic Vision Song Contest. Alien pop groups from all over the cosmos will perform their entries on a show hosted by a silver wigged Terry Wogan, broadcast live from the BBC Television Centre – *on the moon!* Co-host Katie Boyle, who'll be a weightless 150 years of age, will have to learn a few new languages. For she will need to converse fluently in over 1,000 *space languages,* as well as French and German.

Space age Terry

However, some things will never change. Despite the new look contest, nobody will actually watch it, and Norway will still come last.

Cliff yesterday

Everyone knows that the perennial Peter Pan of pop Cliff Richard never ages. He looks exactly the same today as he did when he first shot to stardom in 1952. Indeed, the familiar face of religious Richard will be the only one to survive into the charts of the future. And needless to say, the 84 year old rocker will look exactly the same as he does today, except for even more wrinkles, slightly more leathery skin and a thicker pair of glasses. And a wig.

There'll be no more queueing for pop concerts in the year 2000. Stars of the future will play especially for you – *in your own living room!* Crafty record companies will use advanced bio-technology to 'clone' their best selling stars. And you'll be able to rent a perfect life-like replica of your pop favourite from the corner shop – for around the same price as a video cassette.

BEDROOM

And the good news is that your favourite star will gladly stay the night, and give you a very special *bedroom performance.* The only problem is this extra service will cost saucy pop fans an extra £2,000 a night!

Top record companies are already experimenting with genetic technology, and are believed to have produced a prototype clone of teen sensation Chesney Hawkes. However, that experiment was abandoned after the Chesney clone exploded killing a guitarist during a top secret invitation only experimental test gig at a venue in London.

Chesney clone – blew up

Advances in medical science will mean that by the year 2000 pop stars who have been dead for decades – such as Jimi Hendrix, Buddy Holly and Adge Cutler out of The Wurzels – can be ressurected. 'Born again' stars, dug up from their graves and revitalised by scientists using space chemicals – will be able to continue their careers where they left off.

NAPPY

By the year 2000 Elvis will be top of the charts once more, weighing in at 45 stone, dressed in a silver space age nappy, and recording songs in a specially built giant reinforced toilet/studio in the basement of his Gracelands mansion.

Pop stars have always had a reputation for drink and drugs. But the drugs of the future will be a far cry from the powder and pills they take today. In the future all drugs will have been legalised – except marijuana – and to get a *buzz* in the year 2000 pop stars will simply have to nip into the local newsagent and buy heroin, cocaine or new extra strength *space drugs,* all of which will be available in a 'firework' form.

INJECTIONS

There will be no sniffing, smoking or injections involved. Pop stars will simply return to the privacy of their hotel rooms, light the blue touch paper, and shove the firework up their arse.

A pop star beseiged by groupies yesterday

Of course one great advantage of being a pop star is being able to sleep with lots of groupies. But sadly, by the year 2000 sex will have become a thing of the past. Absolutely everybody will be riddled with AIDS, so sex will all have to be done by computer, in special disease proof space greenhouses on the moon.

In years to come record players – and even CDs – will be dusty relics on a museum shelf. Gone will be the shiny discs we buy today. For record companies have already spent *billions* perfecting the new Strip Disc – a long piece of paper containing musical information in

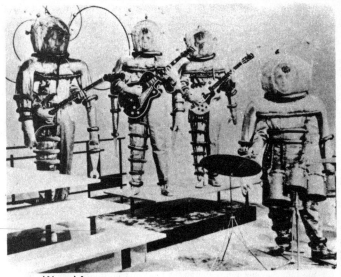

(Above) A pop group
of the future
playing live on Mars

the form of a space age bar code. Simply slip the strip into a pocket sized 'DDDD' (Digital Disc Decoder Deck) and out will come octophonic sound, ten times louder than when it was recorded.

 Believe it or not, record companies are already working on new technology that will eventually supersede the Strip Disc. By the year 2020 they will have done away with records altogether. Instead fans will buy a *'pop' drink* by their favourite band. Simply take a mouthful, and as you swallow your favourite tune will appear in your ears.

ALBUM

Top stars of the future will release their album in three formats – can, bottle or carton. And record companies will boost their summer sales with special limited edition *ice pops*.

 The cumbersome instruments which pop stars carry with them on tour – drums, guitars and pianos – will all be consigned to the rubbish heap of tomorrow by the year 2000. Musicians of the future will need only one walnut sized special purple space crystal, mined on Jupiter, and capable of playing all their music. They will simply *think* the tunes into the crystal, and it will glow and throb, and the tunes will appear, along with a low, rhythmic, humming sound, like on the Tomorrow People.

Scientists from EMI Records are already planning a space voyage to Jupiter to find out whether these crystals actually exist or not.

Radio One jocks
in the year 2000

 Turn on your tranny in the year 2000 and you may be surprised to hear the familiar voices of all your favourite Radio One FM jocks. For in order to preserve their popular but ageing DJs, Radio One controllers will use Dr. Who style technology, removing and pickling their brains before wiring them up to electronic voice boxes. Like the Daleks, the DJ's brains will live in robot bodies, and slide around the corridors of Broadcasting House, bumping into things.

YOU ASK WE ANSWER

"How come the sun is yellow, yet the sky is blue?" asks I. Fell of Gosforth.

Just like a rainbow, ordinary daylight is made up of colours of the spectrum:– red and yellow and pink and green, orange and purple and blue. Light always travels in straight lines, however the sun is a circle. In much the same way water, when examined in a glass appears see through or white, but looks blue when it's in the sea.

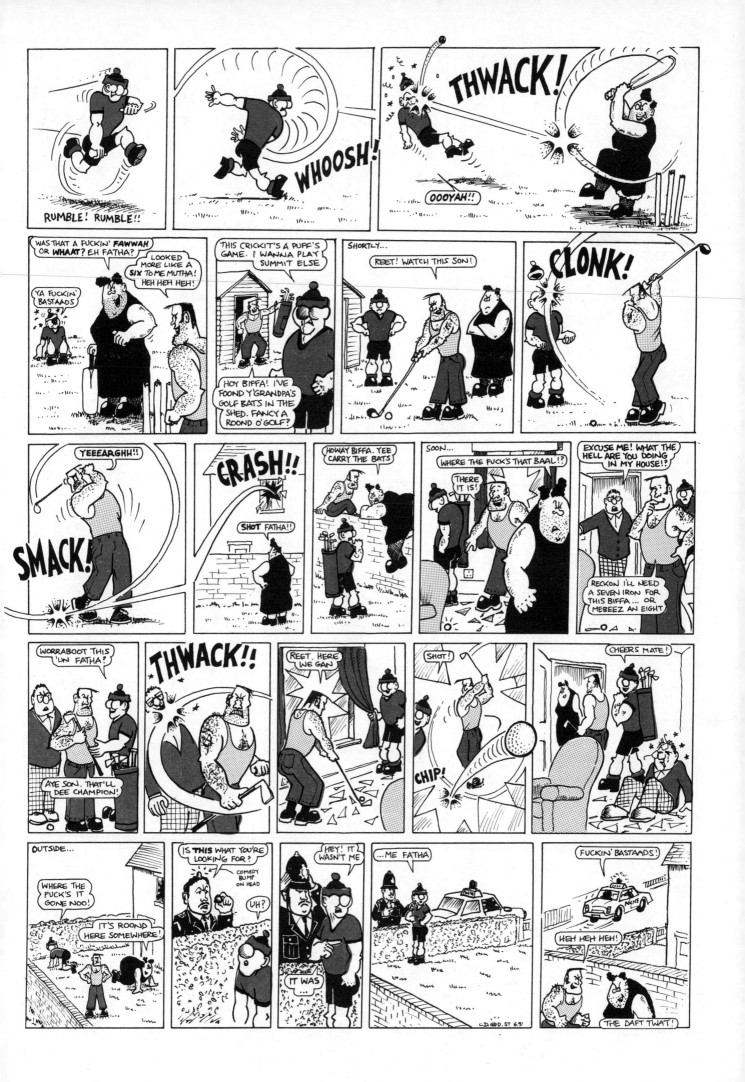

31

WILL FULCHESTER ESCAPE TO VICTORY? DON'T MISS THE NEXT EPISODE - GUEST STARRING BOBBY MOORE, PELE, SYLVESTER STALLONE AND MICHAEL CAINE, WITH SPECIAL GUEST STARS OSSIE ARDILES AND SOME REALISTIC 1940's FRENCHMEN IN FLARES AND WHITE TRAINING SHOES.

LETTERBOX

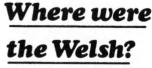

LetterBocks
Viz Commick
P.O. Box 1 PT
Newcasle upon Tyne
NE99 1PT

Oh, what a lovely war

I'm sick and tired of people going on about how horrible the war was. Well I was there, and it was bloody great. I rode on a motorbike, went in a plane, and shot three Germans. I had a marvellous time.

Tom Hobson
Sudbury

It seems fashionable these days to "have a go" at the Queen. With her vast personal fortune of £7 billion, her enormous tax free income, her many horses, servants and that great big yacht, she's an easy target for the "knockers". But the Queen has a very difficult job to do, and I for one would not wish to swap places with her.

Mr. J. Connors
Wembley

Fishing for sympathy

I'm fed up with fishermen who go out in trawlers, catch netfulls of fish and then grumble about the size if their catch, claiming that they can't make a living. My grandad used to go fishing, and he'd be happy if he caught one fish, never mind a whole net full.

B. Bates
Nottingham

Could you please help me settle an argument. My brother insists that TV magician Paul Daniels owns the famous Yorkshire tourist attraction Mother Shipton's cave. But I reckon he's just a bald little twat. Which one of us is right?

Paul Gray
Leeds

TV slap-head Daniels

** You can call a truce Paul, because you're **both** right. Paul bought the cave, near Knaresborough, with it's strange petrifying qualities, several years ago. And at a hairless 4'8", the slap headed TV funster is indeed something of a twat.*

*Do **YOU** have an argument to settle? Perhaps you think TV weathergirl Suzanne Charlton is footballer Bobby's daughter, but a friend insists her dad is brother Jackie. Write to Letterbox and we'll settle your dispute.*

In reply to A. Stapleton's letter (Viz 48). Stop knocking the Welsh. I'm Welsh, and it's fucking great. The trouble with Mr. Stapleton is that he's a twat.

A. Hancock
Morriston, Swansea

Where were the Welsh?

On the subject of the Welsh, where were they during the war while we were sat in our bomb shelters waiting for Hitler to invade? They were sitting pretty, in Wales, singing hymns and growing vegetables. That's where they were.

Annoyed
Middlesex

Once again we read the sickening news that a pensioner has been beaten up in their own home by heartless thugs who stole a paltry sixty pence. How awful that a life can be shattered for such a small amount. It wouldn't be so bad if these people would take a reasonable amount – say £40 or £50. And perhaps some jewellery.

A. Anderson
Hereford

I've changed my mind

Having thought about it for a few minutes – I would now be prepared to swap places with the Queen. The jammy old bitch.

Mr. J. Connors
Wembley

What was Paul McCartney thinking of the day he married that Linda woman? She's not exactly an oil painting is she? She spoils all his records, and now the daft cow won't let him eat sausages.

J. Asher
Hampstead

The McCartneys yesterday

I find that my fingers go through expensive toilet rolls just as often as they do when using the cheaper ones. For that reason I use the cheap ones and use the money I save to buy a bar of soap.

Mrs. E. Sharp
Grunty Fen

When a dog becomes old and infirm it is often the kindest thing to have it put to sleep. In the same way surely it is cruel to keep an old person alive. My father has been lingering in good health now for several years, living alone in a large house in the country. He is now unable to walk more than a few miles before becoming quite short of breath and it is only his many friends, hobbies and interests which keep him going. Surely his family should be entitled to end his suffering and arrange for a doctor to put him out of his misery.

Mr. B. Woodward
Widdle-On-Thames

BISCUITS Alive!

ONE DAY... IT'S NO GOOD— I CAN'T WORK OUT THIS HOMEWORK.

WE'LL HELP!

WHO SAID THAT?

WE DID!

CRUMBS! MY BISCUITS HAVE COME ALIVE!

SEE— TWO PLUS THREE IS FIVE!

WOW - IT'S EASY WITH YOU TO HELP ME!

NEXT DAY... WELL DONE TOMMY— YOU'VE GOT TOP MARKS!

LITTLE DOES HE KNOW - IT'S ALL THANKS TO MY BISCUITS!

They said curiosity killed the cat. Well it didn't. My next door neighbour did.

Linda Longbottom
Walsall

Try doing some work

According to their unions, teachers want higher pay and more esteem for their difficult and highly skilled job. Well perhaps they could earn both if they started working the same hours as normal people instead of going home at 4 o'clock, and gave up 8 weeks or so of their holidays.

Mr. B. McGuire
Hersham

A teacher yesterday

I was amused by A. Gamble's letter (Viz 48) about annoying your neighbours. It was almost as funny as when I first heard it, virtually word for word, twenty three years ago on Marty Feldman's LP "Marty".

J. Wolstenholme
Sheffield

Well spotted, John. There's a crisp tenner on it's way to you. Remember readers, we pay £5 for each letter we publish – and then a tenner to the first person who spots where we stole it from.

I am collecting Shell 'Man in Flight' coins, given free with petrol. Unfortunately my car has been off the road for some time and I do not therefore have occasion to buy a great deal of petrol. I wondered if perhaps some of your readers could help me. I only need 'Louis Bleriot', 'Apollo II' and 'The Wright Brothers' to complete the set, and I am willing to offer the 'Hindenberg' or 'Gordon Banks' in exchange, both of which I have as swaps.

Name and address supplied

Look who's talking

In reply to J. Asher's letter (this issue) – look who's talking. I'd rather marry Paul McCartney and live on a big farm and have loads of money like what I have than marry a tuppenny ha'penny cartoonist who can't even draw properly, and spend my time farting round in a cake shop.

L. McCartney
Mull of Kintyre

Be seen, be safe

I almost ran into the back of a slow moving hearse on a main road recently. As the law requires tractors and other slow moving vehicles to display a flashing amber light, would it not be a good idea for hearses to display similar flashing lights? And perhaps as an extra safety feature they could play a loud, catchy tune, like an ice cream van.

A. Rayleigh
Sidcup

CLEAN SWEEP

British brushes swept the board at the International Brush, Broom and Squidgy Mop Awards in Rio de Janiero this week.

An international panel of adjudicators made up of brush and mop experts from over 150 competing countries judged that British mops were tops.

BRUSHES

Out of the eight competitive categories British brushes took seven coveted Golden Bristle Awards, including Best Adult Tooth Brush (for the Wisdom Senator), Most Versatile Mop (for the Valida Supermop) and Best Toilet Brush (for the Addis Skidbuster 2000).

ENTRY

The British entry was pipped in only one category, the Combined Dustpan and Brush, which was won by the controversial French Compacta Cuisine II brush and pan set, which is alleged to contain parts manufactured in Switzerland.

EXIT

Nevertheless, British brush manufacturers were today bristling with pride, among them Sir Bob Wallace, chairman of the British Brush, Broom and Bucket Confederation. "I've always believed in British brushes", he told us.

FIRE DOOR KEEP CLOSED

According to Sir Bob, who lost a leg during the war, brushes are now Britain's second largest export. "Recent trade figures show that with exports topping £280 billion, brushes are now Britain's second biggest overseas earner, after deck chairs. And nuts" he added. "So that makes them third".

POOR people. Can't afford to eat smoked salmon? Simply eat the rubber off an old table tennis bat.

I. Morris
Tiverton

IF a small child is choking on an ice cube, don't panic. Simply pour a jug of boiling water down its throat, and hey presto! The blockage is almost instantly removed.

Mrs. F. Kippling
Swansea

PRETEND to be Welsh by putting coal dust behind your fingernails, talking gibberish and singing all the time.

Mr. P. Lilburn
Rotheram

IMAGINE you're in London by simply sitting in your car all day with the engine running, occasionally honking your horn, and never actually going anywhere.

G. Foster
Blyth

FREEZE loaves of bread, then sculpt them into animal shapes using a hammer and chisel. Once they've thawed, hey presto! Animal bread zoo figures for the kids.

Mrs. J. Crooks
Grantham

IMPRESS visitors by sitting on their laps, flicking through an animal book and making the appropriate animal noise for each picture.

James Taylor
East Sussex
P.S. This works best if you are under 2 years old.

AVOID bickering and petty arguments by immediately punching anyone with whom you disagree.

S. Taylor
Watford

ANNOY neighbours by buying a TV set exactly like theirs. Then, when they are watching telly, stand outside the window and change the channels using your identical remote control.

Leigh Drake
Portsmouth

MAKE people think you have an expensive car phone by calling them, asking them to repeat everything they say, then hanging up half way through their reply.

Mr. I. Baxter
Exemouth

SHOPKEEPERS. Reduce shoplifting by banning third rate television celebrities from your shop.

A. Price
Worthing

DIGESTIVE biscuits topped with tomato sauce and a small piece of cheese make ideal 'mini pizzas'.

Mrs. J. Crooks
Grantham

MOTORISTS. Keep a foot pump next to your brake pedal, and connect it to an inflatable paddling pool folded on your lap. If you are about to crash, pump rapidly and the inflated pool will cushion you from injury.

J. Thompson
Prestwick

WRAP lightbulbs in sellotape to prevent them shattering in the event that they should fall out of their bayonette fixings for any reason.

Walter Hurst
Hendon

MUMS. Make mealtimes fun by dipping potatoes in food colouring before slicing and frying. Hey presto! Rainbow chips.

Mrs. J. Crooks
Grantham

39

Corn Circle mystery is solved at last

FOOLED YOU!

Red faced scientists may well have to re-write their text books in the light of revelations being made by a former North Yorkshire shepherd.

For Bob Johnson, who retired last year at the age of 70, claims the mysterious phenomenon known as 'Corn Circles' which have baffled the scientific world for months, were all his own handywork. And not only that, he also claims that many other unexplained phenomenon, including UFO's, the Loch Ness Monster and Stonehenge are also down to him.

HOAXES

After years of practical joking, during which Bob has baffled the world's leading scientists with his incredible hoaxes, he has finally decided to own up, and plans to reveal all in a book soon to be published.

THEORIES

His most recent 'mystery', the corn circles, baffled farmers and scientists after the strange, symmetrical patterns appeared in fields the length and breadth of Britain. Various theories were put forward, among them freak weather conditions, UFO landings and rabbits.

But according to Bob, the cause was nothing more sinister than a lawn mower, a pole, and a piece of string. "I got the idea from that cigar advert where Russ Abbot cuts the lawn in his back garden. I just tied my lawn mower to a stick and then sat back, and hey presto".

PUZZLED

Bob claims that the first circles were a practical joke at the expense of local farmers. But when the press began to take an interest, he couldn't resist the temptation of carrying on the hoax. One thing which left puzzled scientists scratching their heads was the vast distances between many of the circles. Overnight one might appear in Scotland, while almost simultaneously another would crop up in the Home Counties. Bob offers the breathtakingly simple explanation.

PEDAL

"I used my bicycle", he told us. "I would ride up and down mostly at nights, so no-one could see me. And of course a pedal cycle is very quiet, so I didn't wake anyone up either".

'It was me all along' says shepherd Bob

Although Bob was proud of some of his cornfield creations, he believes his best hoax to date was Stonehenge. "Yes, I did that as well", he told us. "Mind you, it was a lot harder than the corn circles. At times I wondered whether it would be worth the bother". Working single-handed, it took Bob two days to erect the massive stone pillars which stand in a perfect circle on Salisbury Plain.

CHAIN

"The hardest bit was getting the big ones on the top", he added. "I nearly put my back out doing that". And Bob has finally ended speculation as to how the massive stones were transported to Stonehenge. The answer, according to Bob, was so simple the experts failed to see it. "I got them all there on a sack barrow", he told us.

MUD GUARDS

Bob is always amused when he sees hippies flocking to the stone circle in the mistaken belief that it has great religious significance. "All that nonsense about the summer solstice, and the positioning of the sun makes me laugh. I was just trying to make it into the shape of a smiling face, like those smiley badges, but I ran out of stones".

ENERGY

A lot has been written about the existence of mysterious 'Lay Lines' eminating from Stonehenge, and covering the whole of Britain. The points where these lines cross are said to emit strange and unexplained forces or energy. But Bob has bad news for the theorists. "I made the lay lines as well", he told us. "I just used old lengths of clothes line, hanging from trees".

CHALK

Stonehenge is not the only tourist attraction for which Bob admits responsibility. But two of his other works of art are best viewed from above. "I was looking after my sheep one day when I got bored, so I decided to draw a big horse on the hillside. I only had a few boxes of white chalk on me, so I used that. I thought it would wash off overnight, but years later it's still there".

A corn circle (left), Stonehenge (above) with a flying saucer above it, and a white horse (below).

The chalk horse at Cerne Abbas was so popular with locals that Bob decided to do another big picture, this time in Wiltshire. "I decided to draw a man this time, but it's difficult to get the scale right when you're drawing it all from down on the ground. So I ended up giving him a really big knob, but folks still seem to like it", says Bob.

WASTED

Millions of pounds have been spent researching the mystery of UFO's. But according to Bob, the money has been wasted. "There's no such thing", he told us confidently. "They were just another one of my practical jokes".

STONED

Bob claims that dinner plates, thrown from the top of a hill, are the simple explanation to this phenomenon. And he has bad news also for thousands of tourists and scientists alike who make an annual pilgrimage to Loch Ness in search of the legendary monster 'Nessie'.

PEELED

"I must admit that was me as well", says Bob, raising a finger in admission. "I couldn't resist the temptation". Bob claims he is responsible for almost every Nessie sighting to date. "It's amazing what you can do with a broom stick with a stuffed sock on the end", he told us.

SEGMENTED

If Nessie watchers have found the loch to be a little quiet of late, that is because at 70 Bob no longer feels fit enough for the amount of swimming involved in this clever underwater hoax. Indeed the king of hoaxers now prefers to enjoy a quiet retirement, and has no immediate planes for future stunts. "But next time you see something unusual or unexplained on the TV news, you can bet old Bob's about", he said with a cheeky grin.

Next week: How Bob created holiday havoc in Tibet, using a simple set of circus stilts and a pair of size 8 wellington boots.

AND HERE'S HOW HE DID IT

Borrowing an idea from a TV ad, Bob created corn circle confusion with a simple lawn mower attached to a stick with a length of string. Bob is able to stand by and watch as his makeshift contraption cuts a perfect circle in the corn.

Experts believed that thousands of slaves laboured for many years to winch the huge pillars of Stonehenge into place. "Nonsense", says Bob. Here's how he did it, using a simple sack barrow and a bit of elbow grease.

Scientists have spent years puzzling over this famous snap of 'Nessie' (left) rearing her head above the waters of Loch Ness. Little did they know, swimming just below the surface was joker Bob. Here (right) he re-creates the effect, with a simple broomshank and a stuffed sock.

THE CURSE OF CORONATION STREET

Stars of Britain's longest running TV soap are living in fear after an uncanny catalogue of catastrophe has hit members of the cast of the top rated show.

"There's a curse on The Street and I just know that something terrible is going to happen", said one terrified star who refused to be named.

BIZARRE

Over recent years, in a series of bizarre coincidences, events that have taken place on screen have been uncannily echoed in real life.

REAR-END

* Actress Madge Hindle, alias Street star Renee Roberts, was written out of the script in an horrific car crash. *Only 18 months later Madge was involved in a rear-end shunt at a round-about in Ilkley.* Fortunately the actress was unhurt, but her car suffered £80's worth of damage.

* Only months after script writers penned a scene in which Mavis Wilton's budgerigar died, a double tragedy struck. Actor Bill Waddington, alias Street busybody Percy Sugden, returned to his Osset home to find one of his tropical fish had died. Fifty years earlier, almost to the month, Roy Barraclough's pet dog had been run over by a car.

* Not long after newcomers Jim and Liz McDonald moved into the Street, actor Charles Lawson's real-life brother-in-law put his house up for sale.

SOAP

In 30 years of writing the hit soap script writers have often included story lines concerning marriage break-ups, death and baby dramas – which then come true off-screen.

SHAMPOO

Only years before the break-up of his screen marriage to actress Sue Barlow, actor Mike Baldwin, alias the Street's loveable cockney rogue, romeo rat Johnny Briggs, suffered a real-life argument with his wife Christine.

Although their marriage was in no danger, actor Mike slept on the settee two nights running.

T.V. soap stars fear for their lives

Soap star Jackie Ingram alias the Street's Sharon Taylor (real-life actress Jackie Baldwin) as the soap's loveable romeo rogue (inset) actor Ronnie Biggs, better known to viewers as rag trade rat Ken Baldwin alias on-screen actor Bill Roach yesterday

A scene in which his Street character died of a heart attack signalled a real-life drama for actor Tony Osoba. Real-life Tony, alias on-screen textile boss Pete Ingram, collapsed and died in romeo rat Johnny Baldwin's office.

Only days later, after a round of golf with friends, actor Tony suffered mild chest pains.

SHOWER GEL

Luckily it was a false alarm. Doctors confirmed that Tony was suffering from indigestion as a result of eating his breakfast too quickly. But Tony is still left trembling with fear every time he gets heartburn or flatulence.

BUBBLE BATH

Terrified stars are now pleading with Street bosses to have scripts changed rather than tempting fate. Elizabeth Dawn, alias The Street's Vera Duckworth, successfully begged the show's producers to have a scene in which she visited the opticians written out of the script. For the actress feared she might go blind in real life if the scene were broadcast.

Ironically that scene was replaced by one in which the Duckworth's house was flooded. The next day Dawn, 53, found a tap dripping in her Cheshire house. Not even her local plumber was able to explain the mysterious coincidence.

CURSE

However, the Curse of Coronation Street has not always been bad news for the stars. Some of the uncanny coincidences have happy consequences. For example when actress Barbara Knox, alias Street Star Rita Fairclough, won a three minute trolley dash in the soap's Bettabuys supermarket.

PERIOD

Incredibly, the event was mirrored in real life. *For the very next day actress Barbara won a three minute trolley dash in her local super-market.*

RAG WEEK

And just like her generous on-screen character, big-hearted Barbara donated all her winnings – over £30's worth of groceries – to charity.

44

SD.CD.ST.GPD. Photography Colin D.

PEW! WHAT A SCORCHER

A man claiming to be an ex-vicar sacked by the Church for having sex with a parishoner, is also claiming he was unfairly dismissed.

"I've been made a scape-goat", claims 52-year-old Reg Potter. And now Reg is threatening to blow the lid off some of the seedy goings on he witnessed behind church doors during the six months he was employed as a vicar.

"They sacked me for getting a bit fruity with the customers", says Reg, "but every vicar in the country is *at it*. Why they picked on me I just don't know".

GRAVEYARD

Mr. Potter says he was arrested after churchgoers reported him to police having sex in a graveyard behind his church. "Since when was it illegal to have a bit of fun?" he said yesterday. "That's all I ever did, unlike some vicars I could name".

STEEPLE

According to Mr. Potter sex and adultery are common-place in the Church today. "You wouldn't believe some of the things going on", he told us. "One vicar up the road from me was at it day and night. We used to call him Rev. Randy Bollocks he was that bad. Mind you, he had the biggest *steeple* I've ever seen. The birds used to love to *peel* off in his belfry, and he could *ring their bells* all night long. What a racket! Every now and then you'd hear bells ringing at odd times of the day. Everyone would look puzzled and check their watches, but not me. I knew it was just old Randy Bollocks giving some punter a *special service*.

TOWER

I must admit, I used to *play around a bit* in my belfry. One day I felt a bit kinky in the *bell tower* so I tied my knob to one of the bell ropes. Next thing I knew it was 12 o'clock and in walks the bishop to ring the bells. He caught me red handed, and I ended up getting *tolled off* in more ways than one!

ROTTEN

Another vicar mate of mine fancied his organist some-thing rotten. So one Sunday, after the morning service, he asked her if she fancied a

Rev. Potter - Fruity

quick *session* on another *organ*. She jumped at the chance, I can tell you, *pulling out all the stops*. She had it pumped up and playing in a flash, the dirty old bag.

VICIOUS

Churches are ideal for sex, there's that many different places where you can *do it*. My favourite was always that big tub thing where they Christen all the babies and that. I gave quite a few birds a *bubble bath* in there, I can tell you.

SENSIBLE

And then there's the pulpit, the wooden bit where I say all the prayers. A bit *pokey*, but that's the name of the game! One day another vicar I know (if you're reading this, you know who you are!) was *up* in the pulpit, giving some bird a proper seeing to. Sud-denly, in walks the Bishop.

Sex claim vicar has Bishop's knickers in a twist

My mate nearly shit a brick, I can tell you. He tried to keep as quiet as he could, but this bird started giggling, and gave the game away.

SCABIES

My mate thought he'd get the sack on the spot, but the Bish just smiled and told him to scarper. Next thing you know His Holiness was *on the job*, giving it *six nowt* with this bird. And needless to say, not a word was said afterwards. You see, there's an un-written rule in the Church. You can do it *whenever you like*, with *whoever you like*, as long as you use a blob. That's what I reckon.

ECZEMA

"Mind, if you think vicars are bad, you should see what the left footers get up to. Our local priest was off sick one day (too much sex the night before, probably) so anyway, I had to nip down to his church and do some confes-sions for him. And boy, was I in for a surprise!

RINGWORM

"Waiting outside the con-fessions box was a queue of good looking birds a mile long, all waiting to *reveal all!* Most of them had nothing to confess when they arrived, but that soon changed once I got them inside my little box.

A church yesterday

You wouldn't believe what I got up to. *Mind you, if the Pope ever finds out, some of them birds will be saying "hail Mary" for the rest of their lives, I can tell you.*

DERMATITIS

To be honest I reckon *sex* is the only reason why people bother being vicars in the first place. The pay's crap, and saying prayers isn't exactly the most exciting job in the world. And then there's all the poncy gear you have to wear. I felt a right pratt in some of them dresses. Mind you, come to think of it they're ideal for wearing *on the job*. You can get your tackle out a lot quicker than if you were wearing pants".

DOHBI ITCH

Mr. Potter is claiming £500 compensation from the Church for unfair dismissal. "But I'd accept £100 cash", he told us. When we approa-ched the Church for a com-ment, a vicar appeared and told us we were trespassing. "Go away or I'll call the police", he said.

I'M SICK OF ALL THESE TRAILERS ON THE TELEVISION

DOCTOR, I'VE GOT AN IRON DEFICIENCY

IT'S YOUR FUNERAL!

With heating bills, TV licences, the price of butter and the 'new money' to worry about, old people have enough on their plate these days without having to worry about their funeral expenses.

Of course we all die sooner or later. It's just that old people are usually next. And so saving up for a decent burial is a number one priority for old folk today.

COST

And with the rising cost of kicking the bucket – undertakers, coffins, gravestones, church services and even the buffet to think about – a decent send-off can be beyond the means of many senior citizens.

But here's your chance to *bury* that *worry!* Because we're offering a **FREE FUNERAL** to the winner of this easy-to-enter competition that's open only to old folk. Yes, we'll pay ALL the winner's funeral costs – including a sit-down buffet for up to 100 people. And we'll even put £150 behind the bar to ensure a good time is had by all.

QUESTIONS

All you have to do is answer the following questions by choosing answers A, B or C.

1. In Britain today, what would you identify as being the single most significant economic problem?
a. *A lack of government investment in the economy.*
b. *Interest rates are too high.*
c. *The new five pence coin is too small and fiddly.*

2. How could you complete the following sentence? 'Young people today, they've got no…
a. *…prospect of employment.*
b. *…incentive to continue in full-time education beyond school leaving age.*
c. *…respect. I fought in two world wars etc…*

3. The maximum speed for cars travelling on a motorway is…
a. *60 mph.*
b. *70 mph.*
c. *25 mph.*

4. The old days were much better because you could…
a. *…catch polio at the swimming baths.*
b. *…catch pneumonia while using an outside lavatory.*
c. *…leave your front door open.*

5. What do you think of music these days?
a. *It's all very similar, with a distinctive 'hip hop' back beat, and heavily influenced at present by the Manchester indie scene.*
b. *It's a good, harmless way for the kids to express themselves.*
c. *It's too loud, there's never a tune that you can whistle, and you can't hear the words.*

Old folks Rest In Peace.

We're 'coffin' up for your send~off

6. What do you think of Terry Wogan?
a. *He's overpaid and under-talented.*
b. *He's a fat Irish git.*
c. *Ooh, he's a lovely man.*

7. You're the millionth customer to walk into a shoe shop and you're offered a free pair of shoes as a prize. What would you choose?
a. *A pair of hand stitched Italian brogues.*
b. *A pair of comfortable but expensive suede ladies' court shoes.*
c. *A pair of those ridiculous fleece lined nylon ankle boots. The ones with the thick crepe soles and chunky two inch zips up the side.*

8. You receive an unexpected windfall when an insurance policy matures. You find yourself with £1500 in cash. What would you do with the money?
a. *Invest it in a high interest building society or bank account.*
b. *Spend it on a lovely holiday.*
c. *Shove the lot in a rusty Peak Frean's Teatime Assortment biscuit tin, hide it in your sock drawer, then go downstairs and turn the heating off.*

9. A pimply 14 year old wearing a bright purple Shell suit calls at your door, says he's from the gas board and asks to read the meter. What would you do?
a. *Ask to see some form of indentification.*
b. *Close the door and call the police.*
c. *Let him in and make him a cup of tea while he ransacks the house looking for your rusty biscuit tin full of money.*

10. You meet an old friend in the street and stop for a chat. During the conversation would you…
a. *Forcefully put forward your own opinions and tend to dominate the conversation.*
b. *Listen intently to what the other person says, interjecting occasionally with relevant points.*
c. *Stare blankly at the other person, nodding in agreement and slowly murmuring "yes" before repeating the last word of every sentence.*

Please note this competition is open to old people only. Send your answers, on a postcard, to 'It's Your Funeral' Competition, Viz, P.O. Box 1PT, Newcastle upon Tyne NE99 1PT. (You can buy a postcard, together with a stamp, from the Post Office where you collect your pension. But you'll be surprised at the price of stamps these days). The winner will be notified by post in big, clear, easy-to-read writing.

20 THINGS YOU NEVER KNEW about INSECTS

They're here, there and everywhere. Summer's here again, and so are insects. Whether you're walking in Wakefield Westgate, picnicking in Pontefract park or hitch hiking in High Heaton, just pick up a rock and there they are – hundreds of little insects, ranging from big to small, fat to thin, and with any number of legs. Girls hate them, babies eat them. But what exactly are insects? What do they do and where do they live? How much do you really know about these miniature marvels of Mother Nature. Here's twenty creepy crawly things you never knew about insects . . .

① You'll never drown an insect by holding its head under water – no matter how hard you try. That's because insects breath through special lungs – called *trachea* – which are in their arse.

② Next time you cross the road as well as looking out for cars, keep an eye peeled for the Deer-Bot fly. For it's the world's fastest flying insect, travelling in short bursts at up to 36 miles per hour! That's faster than the prescribed speed limit for a motor vehicle travelling in a built-up area.

③ Insects live in the most unusual places. For example moths, which live in wardrobes, spiders, which live in the bath, and cockroaches, which live in chinese restaurants.

④ And Dung beetles, which live up cows' arses.

Clare Short.

⑤ The noisiest insect of all is the Trumpet beetle of Papua New Guinea. Mating pairs make a noise often compared to a washing machine in its 'spin' cycle. An endangered species, the few remaining examples are protected by strict conservation laws. Residents living near the insects' breeding grounds can claim government grants enabling their homes to be fitted with secondary double glazing.

⑥ We've all cursed after tripping on a broken paving stone. But next time you do it, don't blame the council. Blame insects. For as well as living under rocks, many insects set up home under pavements and footpaths, their constant to-ing and fro-ing causing damage which costs local authorities an estimated *£19 million* a year in crack repairs alone.

⑦ During the swinging sixties it was all the rage to name pop groups after insects, the best example of course being 'The Beatles' . . . The only other one we can think of is Buddy Holly and the Crickets.

⑧ Next time you're in Australia and you need to go to the toilet, check under the seat before you sit down. For each year over 2,000 unfortunate Aussies die from insect bites. The Black Widow spider nests under toilet seats, and repeatedly bites the arse of any unsuspecting victim who sits down to use the loo. Within ten minutes of being bitten the poor toilet-goer develops a huge pan-handle, and dies.

⑨ Another dangerous insect, the bee, can only sting once, and then it dies. That's because the poor insect pulls its ringpiece inside out while flying away afterwards.

⑩ Mind you, another kind of 'B', phone company 'B.T.' can sting you repeatedly. Every time you pick up the fucking phone to be precise.

⑪ Like us, bees have a Queen. However, unlike our Queen, the Queen bee doesn't sit on her arse all day, occasionally waving at people.

⑫ And another thing. The Queen bee's offspring go out and become useful members of their community, working hard, instead of going skiing for 8 months every year.

⑬ And if bees had universities, which they don't, but *if* they did, the Queen bee's kids would have to qualify for entry on merit, instead of getting into Oxford with one bloody 'A' level in dance or something ridiculous like that.

⑭ Getting back to bees, the Bee Gees are another sixties pop group with an insect in their name, although ironically 'Bee Gee' was never intended as an insect reference. It is, of course, the initials of the 'Brothers Gibb'.

⑮ Insects hit the pop headlines again in the early eighties when Adam Ant and The Ants dressed up as swashbuckling highwaymen, complete with red indian war paint, and invited the record buying public to "come and join our insect nation", whatever that meant.

⑯ Like so many post punk pop stars of that era, among them Gary Numan, Howard Jones and Nick Heyward, Adam Ant (real name George O'Dowd) later disappeared up his own arse.

⑰ One exception was of course Limahl out of Kajagoogoo, who by all accounts dissappeared up . . .

⑱ Getting back to insects, if you visit a flea circus, you can expect to see fleas, tied up with fuse wire, perform a variety of spectacular and exciting tricks. (However, if you go to a flea market you can expect to be charged about eight quid for an old bottle with soil on it.)

⑲ If someone tells you they've got 'butterflies', they don't necessarily own a collection of lepidopterous large winged insects. More likely they're suffering from a mild attack of nerves. Or alternatively they might be referring to a video recording of Carla Lane's 'gentle' BBC TV sit-com, starring Wendy Craig and Geoffrey Palmer. Although that's a bit unlikely, as it was a heap of shite. Just like Bread. And everything else she does, for that matter.

Linda McCartney – guest starred in TV's 'Bread'.

⑳ Some parasitic forms of flea are unable to live independent lives. Instead, they live on the back of a 'host' beetle upon whom they rely entirely for their survival.

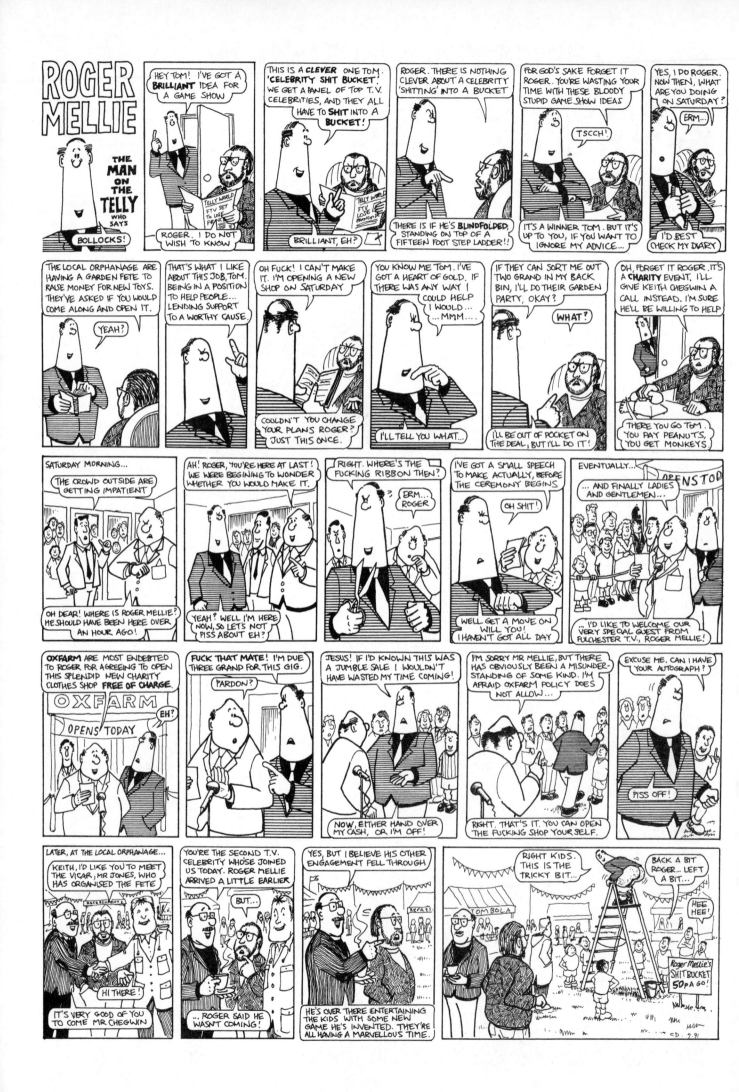

51

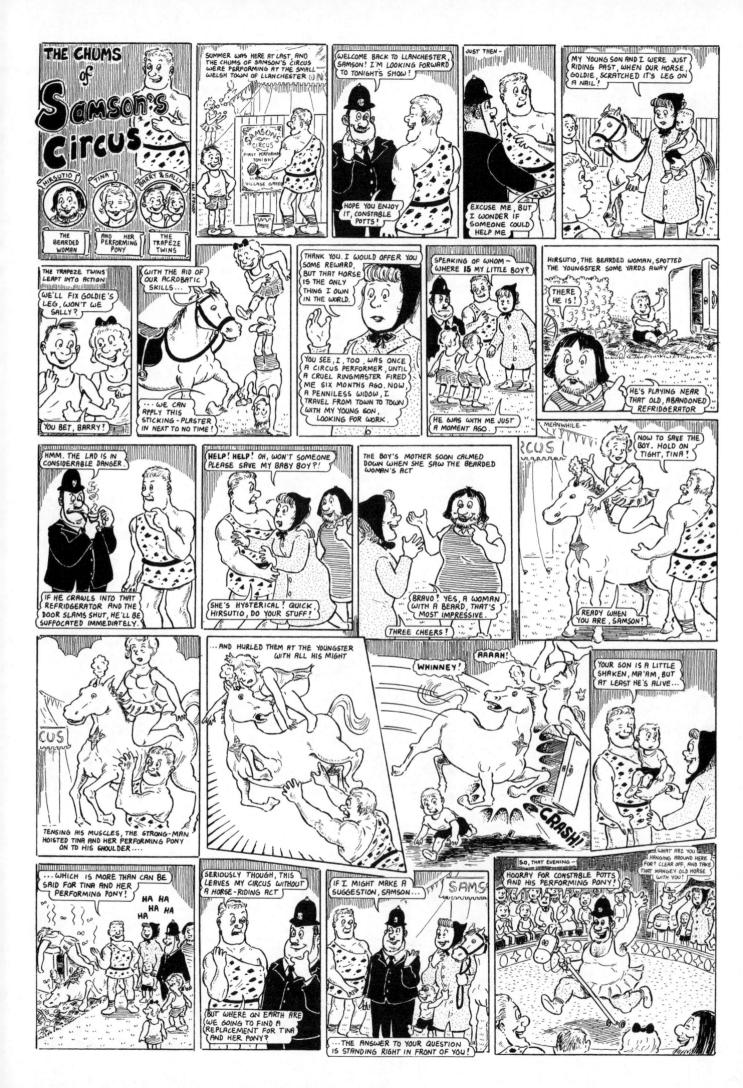

KINKY SEX PROB
OF THE STARS

Although none of us like to admit it, we all suffer from peculiar, and at times entertaining, personal problems which affect our love lives. We all have our own secret little sexual hang up.

And that goes for the stars as well. For you can be sure that many of the top names in show business have sexual difficulties which they refuse to discuss with even their closest friends.

RESPECT

We respect every individual's right to privacy, and we would never reveal information which could cause distress or embarrassment to a named celebrity. Instead, we asked a top sex therapist and problem expert to consider several *hypothetical* cases.

YO PACE

We asked our expert to imagine that a number of top TV stars have come to him with their own sexual problems. And in each case we asked him what advice he would give. As a result for the first time ever we are able to give you an exclusive and fascinating insight into the **IMAGINARY SEX PROBLEMS OF THE STARS.**

*Having invested a large sum of money in an all-rubber skin diving suit, Radio One DJ **SIMON BATES** finds that he is unable to achieve sexual arousal whilst wearing the costume. The idea of rubber gear turns him on, but in practice his wet suit is a flop as he ends up flapping around hopelessly on the bed, flippers waving in the air. As a result his partner is turned off, and Simon's sex life takes a dive.*

There are many different forms of sexual fetish of which rubber is one of the most common. Wearing tight fitting rubber clothing can

SEXY SIMES

act as a powerful stimulant, and if both sexual partners approve, there is nothing wrong or harmful in the behaviour. However, I would suggest that DJ Simon really has jumped in at the deep end. If the idea appeals to him, he should begin by introducing rubber to his lovemaking gradually. At first, for example, he could try wearing a rubber glove.

CHILL OUT

After a while he might want to try a shower cap, and then perhaps a pair of wellington boots. Providing this proves successful he should continue building up slowly towards wearing his full wet suit, getting used to the sensual feel of rubber on his body a little at a time. A liberal covering of talcum powder will prevent chaffing when Simon eventually puts on the full costume.

RUBBER

If, after experimenting, Bates finds that rubber simply does not live up to his expectations then my advice would be, "perhaps rubber just isn't for you Simon. Try something else – leather and

chains, women's underwear or perhaps a school girl's uniform complete with satchel and hat". Whatever the outcome I would wish Simon well, and hope that he and his partner have many 'golden hours' of sexual experimentation.

*Zany 'Fools and Horses' actor **RODNEY LYND-HURST** keeps losing his girlfriends. He is suffering from the embarrassing condition of premature ejaculation. Extremely premature ejaculation – usually before he's even got the girl back to his flat. Indeed, the 'plonker' in question often goes off without warning, in restaurants, cinemas and in the back of taxi cabs, leaving red faced Rodney looking a proper fool. What advice could you offer?*

The most common causes of premature ejaculation are anxiety and nervousness, common among youngsters like Rodney. My advice would be "relax". Instead of going to the cinema, why not invite girls for a swim at the local baths? Cold water should keep things under control. And afterwards keep those wet trunks on beneath your trousers. If your alarm gets raised in a restaurant don't panic. Simply order a bottle of champagne. Then, while your partner sips the bubbly, discreetly slip the contents of the ice bucket down your pants. This will allow a 'cooling off' period until you get home.

*Straight-faced TV news hound **JEREMY PAXMAN** writes to you for advice. In his letter he explains that during a meal at his girlfriend's parents' house, the girl's mother played footsie with him under the table. Then, that evening, while he was sleeping on the settee the girl's mother crept downstairs and began kissing him. "The next thing I knew we were making love", writes Jeremy. "It was fantastic – better than anything I had ever experienced before. This woman was twice my age, and she taught me things I*

DON'T THESE TRA
KEEP YOU AWAKE

NO. I'M A VERY
HEAVY SLEEPER.

.EMS

It's the problem page with a difference

didn't know were possible", his imaginary letter might continue.

MOTHER

However, Paxman feels guilty and ashamed, and he now fears that he could lose his girlfriend. "I wish this had never happened. I love my girlfriend but her mother keeps asking me to go out with her, and she wants to have sex with me again. But I don't want to have sex with her because I love my girlfriend too much. What will I do?"

Newscaster Jeremy has certainly got himself into quite a mess. His girlfriend's mother is equally to blame, but Jeremy has made a big mistake allowing himself to be seduced by this older woman. Under no circumstances should he see the mother again. And if he wants to continue his relationship with his girlfriend, he will have to come clean and face the consequences.

LETTER

In the circumstances I think it would be best if he explained what had happened in a letter, and then allow some time for both himself and his girlfriend to think things over. After a while she may forgive him, like in that film with Dustin Hoffman, and things could return to normal. But if she cannot, and she refuses to see Jeremy again, he must understand her feelings and accept that decision.

*Award winning TV producer **DESMOND WILCOX** secretly confides that his wife, 'That's Life' presenter **ESTHER RANTZEN**, has to 'have it' fifteen times a day. Desmond simply cannot cope, so in order to satisfy her lust for love, Esther has embarked on a bonking frenzy. Indeed, she has bonked her way through the entire cast and crew of the 'That's Life' programme in one afternoon. Overnight she has become a sizzling sex bomb, and desperate Desmond turns to you for advice.

Differing sexual appetites can lead to a great many problems in a relationship. Esther's appetite has obviously increased greatly and this could be caused by a variety of things. At her age she may feel she has reached a twilight period in her love life, and so she wants to 'get it' as much as possible before it's too late. Simultaneously she may feel that Desmond's love wick has been dampened by the onset of old age. My advice to him would be, "carry on as normal as if nothing has happened". For example, if Esther makes love to a waiter while you're dining in a restaurant, just ignore them. Carry on with your meal. By behaving in this way Esther is, in effect, handing you your pink ticket. If she can do it, then *so can you*. Get out there and fill your boots.

TORY 'TOPS FOR TOILETS' CLAIM

People are using the toilet more under a Tory government. That's the claim being made by one Government spokesman as election fever begins to set in.

Tory M.P. Anthony Regents-Park claims that under a Labour Government Britain's population weren't passing as many stools as they do today. "Prior to 1979 people either weren't using the toilet enough, or they weren't using it properly." said Mr. Regents-Park yesterday.

ROUTINE

"After 12 years of Conservative rule Britain's toilet routine has never been so good", he told us. "People are passing firmer stools, more regularly, and bottom wiping has therefore become less of a problem".

VISITS

In fact, Mr. Regents-Park claims that despite making **MORE** visits to the toilet, we are now spending **LESS** time there, as a result of quicker wiping. But he had this warning for voters. "Under a Labour Government stools would be loose, infrequent and very difficult to wipe up

Sir Antony Regents-Park

afterwards. And that would be a step backwards for Britain".

PROBLEMS

Labour spokesman Derek Twatt dismissed the Government claims as "ridiculous", and blamed 12 years of Tory Government for problems such as diarrhoea and haemorrhoids.

INCREASE

"Both the shits and bum grapes are on the increase as a direct result of this Tory Government's policies", he told us.

58

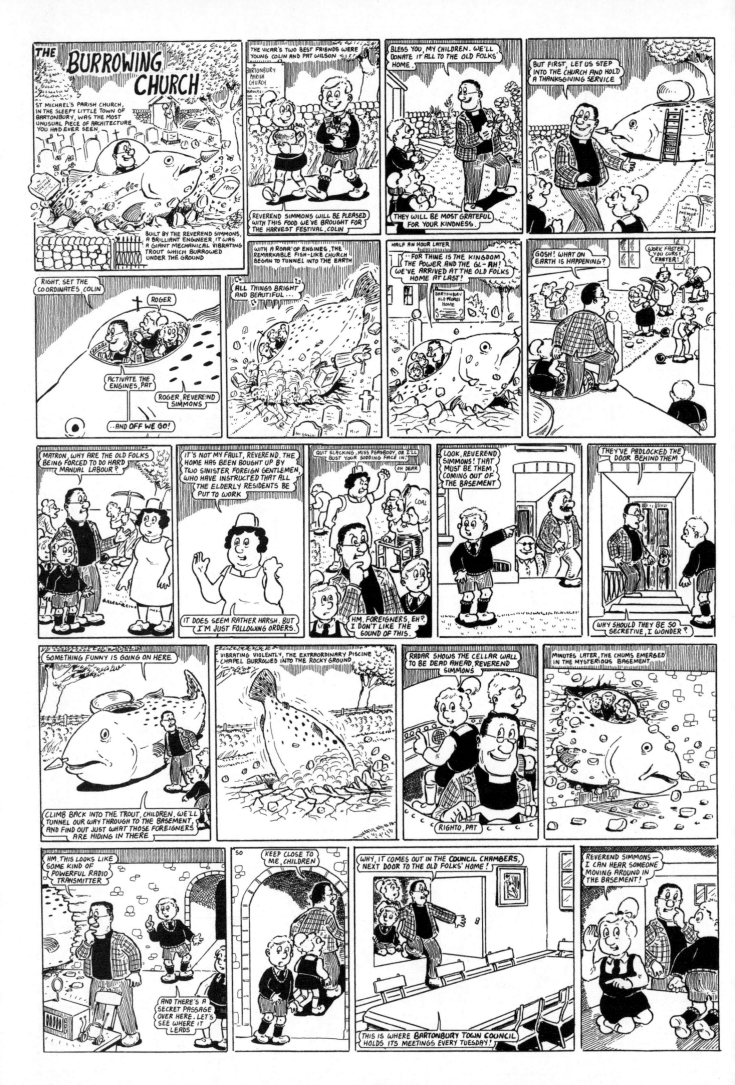

QUEEN FOR A DAY

In recent months there has been increasing controversy over the role of Britain's monarchy. Are the Royal Family paid too much? Should the Queen pay income tax? Do the Royals *really* justify their massive salaries? Is it right that the Queen should be paid £7 billion a year for opening a few bridges and waving at people?

Many people now feel that the monarchy should perform a more useful function in a modern democratic society. But what useful function could they perform? We decided to ask some of the top stars of TV and show business what **THEY** would do if they were **QUEEN FOR A DAY**.

What would the stars do if they were on the throne

JOHN ALTMAN

After playing drug addict Nick Cotton in TV's East Enders, John knows the kind of problems drugs like heroin can cause. Not surprisingly he believes the Queen should use her priviliged position to help tackle the problem of drug addiction in the inner cities.

SCHOOLS

"If I was the Queen I would visit schools in deprived areas and lecture the kids on the harm that drugs can do", John told us. John would use special 'Royal Drama Workshops' to get his message across.

"I think kids would take notice of the Queen, especially if they were able to join in a role playing situation in which they could experience for themselves the problems that drugs can cause. Hopefully some kids may be encouraged to take up drama as a career, so that perhaps one day they could be in East Enders like I am".

RAY ALAN

Together with his comedy ventriloquist's dummy Lord Charles, Ray is a familiar sight on Britain's TV screens. A keen supporter of the monarchy, Ray would be delighted to accept an invitation to be 'Queen for a day'.

DUMMY

"I think a ventriloquist's dummy would be a real asset to me as Queen", Ray told us. "You see, the Queen must be polite at all times, so if, for example, I was to yawn during a conversation with someone important, I could use my dummy to turn it into a joke".

Ray would love the opportunity of making the Queen's Christmas Day speech.

BORING

"The Queen's speeches are always boring, so I would leave all the talking to Lord Charles. Meanwhile, I could get all the laughs by drinking a glass of water", Ray quipped.

LINDA McCARTNEY

Busy Linda combines a career as an accomplished musician with being Britain's top vegetarian chef. But Liverpudlian Linda would still find time to be Queen for a day. Not surprisingly, the first thing on her royal agenda would be to ban sausages!

DRUMSTICK

"Meat is murder", said Linda. "Every time you eat a turkey drumstick you are eating a slab of fear". So all meat products would be banned during her reign and boxes of veggie burgers would be marked 'By appointment to her Majesty the Queen'.

Another issue on which Linda feels strongly is charity. "I don't think the Queen does enough to raise money for charity", Linda told us. "If I was Queen I would get my friends and organise a car boot sale to raise money for needy causes".

PATTIE BOULAYE

Best known as the star of various theatre, cabaret and TV appearances, Pattie believes the role of Queen would suit her down to the ground.

"I'd love to be Queen", she admitted. "And if I was I'd clear out some of her wardrobes". **OUT** would go the Queen's boring dresses, skirts, hats and coats. And **IN** would come new sexy lingerie, giving the Queen a sizzling new look for the nineties. And with Pattie as Queen, there'd be even more shocks in store for tourists visiting London.

"I would make the household cavalry wear sexy G strings instead of stuffy uniforms", Pattie revealed. "And I'd have the changing of the guard ceremony choreographed. I would appear on horseback, wearing a sexy red leotard, singing Jesus Christ Superstar, then, at the end, there would be a big firework display".

WHAT WOULD YOU DO?

What would **YOU** do if you were Queen for the day? How would you put your power and influence to good use for the benefit of your country? What changes would you make to the monarchy in order to improve the system?

Write and tell us, on the back of a postcard. Whoever sends us the most innovative and original idea will be granted their wish. For we will make you **QUEEN FOR A DAY.**

The winner will travel to London first class, all expenses paid. Then you'll be given a hat, and a coat, and a little handbag, and left to wander the streets all day, talking to passers-by, shaking hands with old ladies, and waving at people to your heart's content. Then, when you've finished, you can make your own way home. Send those entries to 'Queen For A Day', P.O. Box 1PT, Newcastle upon Tyne, NE99 1PT, to arrive by next Friday.

Letterbox

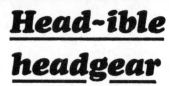

LetterBocks
Viz Commick
P.O. Box 1 PT
Newcasle upon Tyne
NE99 1PT

It's the people's page that's going forward with Britain – <u>into the year 2000</u>!

Ginger nuts make me see red

Congratulations to Viz for having a go at ginger people. How long have the vast majority of us normal folk had to put up with these red-headed nincompoops. Let's have more attacks on carrot tops in the future.

S. Dressing
Huddersfield

Isn't it amazing the authenticity of the soap opera 'East Enders'. Why, only last week I rented out my mothers house to several interested parties and murdered the local publican.

K. Lewis
Widcombe

As old as you feel

A postman called at our door with a package addressed to 'Mrs. P. Wall'. "Is your mother in?" he asked. His remark made my day. He obviously thought I was too young to be married. I was flattered, until I remembered I am in fact 12, and the parcel was indeed for my mother.

Mary Wall
Wallington

That man was wrong

In reply to B. McGuire's letter (issue 49) concerning teachers. Most teachers *do not* go home at 4'o'clock, and if they do they take work with them. Most of them *do not* have 8 weeks holiday. Courses must be taken to improve their teaching standards. I wonder what Mr. McGuire does for a living.

Mrs. Hughes
Huyton, Merseyside
(Non-teacher)

The other night I dreamt I was lying naked in bed next to beautiful 'Woman of Substance' actress Jenny Seagrove. Imagine my surprise when I awoke the next morning to find that I was.

M. Winner
London

Why oh why can't supermarkets arrange their goods in alphabetical order on the shelves. I'm sick and tired of spending hours on end looking for the toilet tissue. I suggest a similar system to that used by libraries, with all items being indexed for easy reference. Shoppers could go first to the relevant reference numbers against each item on their list. Oversized goods, such as large cereal packets or washing up powders could be kept on a separate shelf, and newly arrived or discounted goods could be kept on a special trolley, similar to the 'just returned' book rack.
Customers could be given tickets allowing them 6 purchases at a time, thus doing away with check out queues caused by greedy customers who pile their trolleys high with shopping. And their could be small fines for shoppers who fail to return their trolleys to the trolley park within a given time period.

L. Soakers
Chief Librarian
Fulchester Civic Library

Why oh why do animal rights extremists make such an awful fuss about animal testing? If I was a dog or a rabbit I'd be only too pleased to receive lots of free cigarettes or cosmetics.

D. Cassedy
Trouserville

I'll tell you what would sort out these 'lesbians'. A bloody good shagging, that's what.

C. Stack
Manchester

Climatology inaccuracy

They say 'every cloud has a silver lining'. That's nonsense. Clouds consist of condensed moisture, and the presence of silver is a physical impossibility.

R. Twig
Southend

In reply to Mrs. Hughes' letter (this issue), what does she know? She admits she isn't a teacher. I *am* a teacher, and I do fuck all. I don't start till after half nine, and I'm usually home by four. Like most teachers, I spend all day in the staff room, smoking. Mrs. Hughes is talking out of her arse.

A. Teacher
Name and address supplied.

I bought a light bulb for 2d in 1963 and put it in my bathroom. 28 years later and it's still there. Now that's what I call value for money! (Unfortunately the bulb 'popped' early in 1964, but other than that it is still as good as new.)

R. Valleys
Chichester

Head-ible headgear

"I'll eat my hat if I win", I said to a friend before entering a competition recently. In the event I did win, and sure enough – I ate my hat. It was an edible hat making competition! Do I win £5?

V. Window
Pontefract

Our 3-year old grand daughter is a constant source of amusement. "I wish you'd hurry up and die, you wrinkly old ratbag, and leave all your money to mammy so she can buy me some toys", she said to her grandmother recently.

R. Void
Northwich

Astronomy inaccuracy

Who said 'money makes the world go around'. I was always taught that it rotated as a result of magnetic forces acting on the axis linking the North and South pole.

P. Moore
Lower Flinch

I can drink 15 pints in an evening, eat a huge Indian takeaway, watch telly till three in the morning, and *still* give my missus a bloody good seeing too before I go to sleep. Can any of your readers beat that?

W. Plate
Cramlington

AS YOU CAN SEE, THERE'S A LOT OF SPACE IN THE LIVING ROOM.

Top Tips

CUT along the edge of a tea bag and empty out the tea to make an ideal After Eight mint cosey.

A. Asda
Castleford

SAVE electricity on freezing winter nights by unplugging your fridge and placing the contents on your doorstep.

L. Lipton
Lanarkshire

MAKE your own tea bags by pouring tea into an After Eight mint envelope and stapling it closed. Then puncture the sides 2000 times with a pin.

A. Asda
Castleford

PARKING problems? Tie a balloon to the front bumper of your car, and Sellotape a drawing pin to the rear wall of your garage. When you hear the balloon burst, apply the brakes.

Q. Quicksave
Quebec

WIG wearers. Secure your toupe in high winds by wearing a colourful party hat with an elasticated chin strap. Carry a balloon and a bottle of wine, and you'll pass off as a innocent party goer.

F. Fine-Fare
Fulchester

CENTRALLY position your car within the garage by fixing a torch to the exact centre of the bonnet. Then line up the beam with a small target placed in the centre of the rear garage wall, and drive slowly forwards. (Until the balloon bursts).

Q. Quicksave
Quebec

TRANSFORM your garage into a 'drive-in' restaurant by sitting in your car, lowering your window and demanding that your wife brings you a cup of tea, on roller skates.

S. Safeway
Surbiton

DON'T waste money on expensive toilet freshners. Simply hang pleasant smelling herbal tea bags over the rim of the loo, and every time you flush – hey presto! Your toilet fills with lovely tea.

A. Asda
Castleton

AN OLD television with a toaster inside makes an ideal microwave oven. For making toast.

W. M. Low
Lowick

ATTACH a Christmas cracker by two pieces of string, one to your front bumper and one to your garage wall, the total length being equal to that of your garage. Then reverse your car. When the cracker explodes, stop, get out of the car, and close the garage door.

Q. Quicksave
Quebec

CYCLISTS. Avoid getting flies in your eyes by making a pair of goggles out of two tea strainers.

P. Presto
Preston

PREVENT cats from eating the contents of your fridge whilst they are standing on the doorstep by surrounding them with chicken wire.

L. Lipton
Lanarkshire

MUFFLE the sound of your Walkman when travelling on public transport by placing a tea bag between your headphones and each ear.

A. Asda
Castleton

Tinker, tailor, weather girl, train driver

Driving a train is every schoolboy's dream. But it would be the last job you'd expect to find a TV weathergirl doing.

For it is an almighty jump from reading the weather on TV to driving a train. But, unlikely as it seems, that's exactly what it would be if Trish Williamson quit her £80,000 job on ITV and went to work on the railways.

SKILLS

Of course the skills required for presenting a live TV weather forecast are completely different from those required for driving express trains at speeds of up to 140 miles per hour. A weather girl must be tidy, presentable and cool under pressure, with a good knowledge of weather essential. Hardly the ideal qualifications for driving a train!

INTRIGUED

So we were intrigued to know whether Trish, who at 33 is happily married with two kids, would be at all interested in driving a train for a living. A spokesman for ITV sounded almost as surprised as we were when we mentioned the idea. "I have no idea what you are talking about", we were told.

TV girl Trish.

Meanwhile tight-lipped Trish wasn't giving away any clues. Last night she was 'too busy' to talk to us. Perhaps she was polishing her driver's whistle? Who knows.

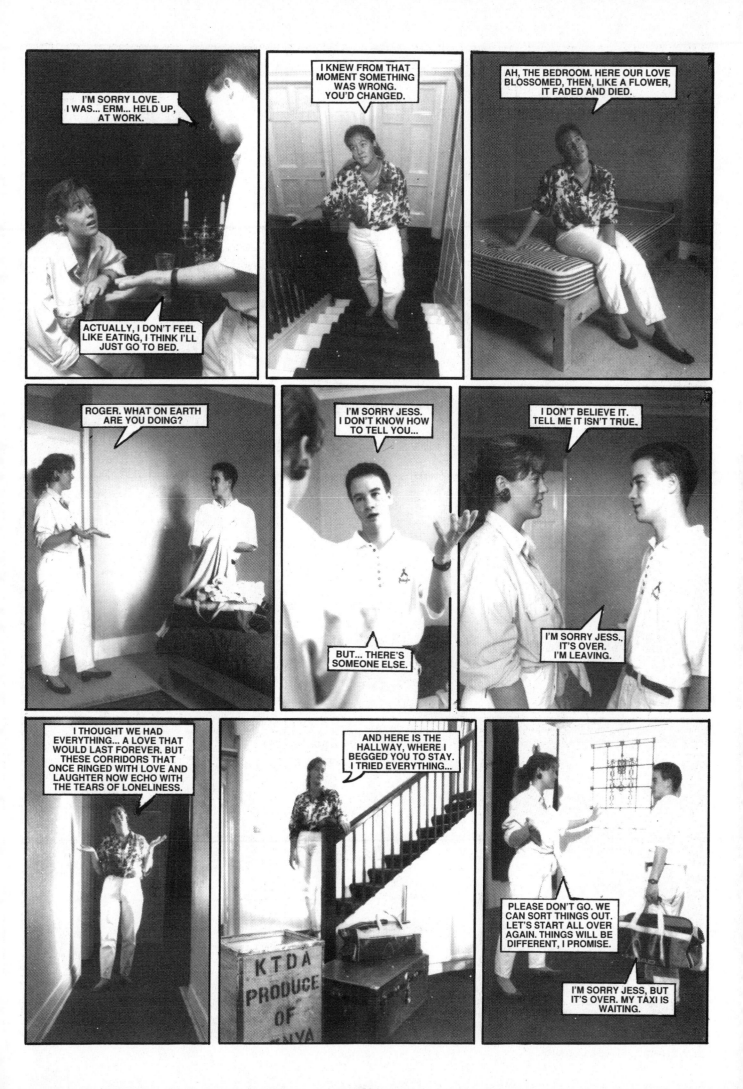

SD.CD.GPD.ST. Photography by Colin D.

20 THINGS YOU NEVER KNEW ABOUT... DOGS

Woof! Woof! Some dogs yesterday

It's a dog's life, or so the saying goes. And never more so than at Christmas, when millions of people across the country open up their Christmas stockings to find unwanted puppies inside.

But before you bag up your unwanted pooch and chuck it in the nearest river, why not stop for a moment and think. How much do you **really** know about our four legged friends? For instance, did you know that...

1 A dog's sense of smell is ten million times more sensitive than that of a human being. This means that a dog standing in Trafalgar Square could smell a kipper – on the Moon!

2 If a vet picks up your dog, never ask him to 'put it down', because if you do he'll kill it with a needle in the back of the neck, and send you a bill for £14. That's because the expression 'to put a dog down' means to kill it with a needle in the back of the neck, and send you a bill for £14.

3 Americans love their dogs, and Los Angeles is the dog capital of the world. There are dog hairdressers, dog psychiatrists and even a dog restaurant, open exclusively to dogs. But any dog can't just walk in. Tables must be booked 3 months in advance, and prices start at $200 (£800) for a bowl of onion soup.

4 A hot dog isn't a dog with a temperature. Nor is it a stolen dog, wanted by the police. It is in fact a stale sausage sandwich with onions and mustard on it, often sold outside football matches for £5 each.

5 Hot dogs with sausages in them shouldn't be confused with sausage dogs. A sausage dog isn't a sandwich, it's a small, sausage shaped dog with tiny legs that only just manage to keep it off the floor.

6 The world's smallest dog is the chiwawa, the smallest ever recorded example belonging to Kalvin Phillips, the world's smallest man. His parents presented him with a puppy 'Shorty' at Christmas 1952. The dog weighed a microscopic 4 grammes, but Kalvin got bored and drowned him the next day – in a thimble of water.

7 If you bend down to examine a 'dog end' on the pavement, you definitely wouldn't be looking up the back end of a beagle, or examining the arse of an alsation. In fact, the chances are you would pick it up and smoke it! That's because a dog end is the disregarded portion of a cigarette.

8 And if your dog end was covered in the previous owner's saliva, you'd probably tut and remark that it had a 'duck's arse' on it.

9 Although they can be attractive animals, calling a girl a 'dog' would not be taken as a compliment. That's because 'dog' is a derogatory term used to describe an ugly woman.

10 And so is 'boiler'.

11 In cave man days dogs were much bigger than the ones we know today. Although little remains of these pre-historic dogs, we know that they had enourmous jaws, big enough to bury the massive dinosaur bones which scientists are still discovering to this day.

12 The Queen is Britain's number one dog lover, and her 700 Corgis are treated like royalty. No expense is spared. Each week all 700 dogs are taken to high class hairdressers Truefitt & Hill of Old Bond Street for a shampoo and trim. Indeed, the Queen spends £60,000 a year on cotton buds alone, which she uses to wipe the dog's bottoms.

13 Unlike kids today, dogs are prepared to get up off their backsides and do an honest day's work. Sheep dogs chase sheep around hills, fox hounds chase foxes around hills, police dogs bark at football fans, and specially trained sniffer dogs are used by customs officials to detect tiny amounts of drugs – concealed up people's bottoms.

14 The law no longer requires dogs to be licensed. However you do need a license to own a pub, a television, a car or a fish.

15 Or a gun.

16 But you *don't* need a license for a *gun dog*. Because a gun dog isn't a gun. It is in fact a dog.

17 Dogs are the world's most intelligent animals, apart from dolphins. And parrots. Indeed, the first man in space was in fact – a dog! On the 4th of October, 1957, history was made when Russian poodle Rin Tin Tin took off on board the Soviet's Sputnik rocket. Sadly, after three days orbiting the earth the heroic hound exploded.

18 If someone says 'it's raining cats and dogs' you needn't expect a downpour of domestic pets. Unless you live in Bolivia! For in 1932 meteroligists there were baffled when a football match between Ixiamas and Cotagaita was abandoned by the referee after it had started rainings *dogs* – and *frogs!* And fish as well.

19 Ask a prostitute in the Kings Cross area of London for 'doggies', and she'd be unlikely to hand you a basket of puppies. The chances are she'll get down on her hands and knees and avail herself to you for sexual intercourse – from behind. That's because 'doggies' etc. etc. etc.

20 Ask the same lady for a 'topless hand shandy' and she'll probably get her tits out and pull you off for £25.

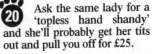

73

WINDS OF CHANGE

Blow me! We'd all better hang on to our hats if the latest forecasts from Britain's weather chiefs are to be believed.

For according to experts, by the year 2000, terrifying tornado force winds gusting at speeds of up to 1,000 miles per hour will turn the nation's streets into a no-go area for pedestrians.

WATCHDOGS

Met office forecasters fear that recent trends towards windier weather are set to continue. And Government weather watchdogs, aware of dramatic changes in our climate, have commissioned a comprehensive report on the problem from top boffins at Reading University's Department of Wind. And the 200 page report makes grim reading for people planning to go outdoors in the year 2000.

COOK REPORTS

For it predicts that continual high winds will bring about dramatic changes in the way we live our lives.

GONE will be high rise buildings. In their place, low, rounded, wind cheating, 'Smartie' shaped structures will spring up in their thousands.

GONE will be the cars of today. The 'windmobile' of the future will be powered by sails, and instead of wheels it will have big rubber suckers to hold it to the ground.

And **GONE** will be the extravagant fashions of today. Wind-proof clothing specialists will replace fashion boutiques on Britain's gale battered High Streets. Shoes will be heavy, like diving boots, with electro magnetic soles to anchor the wearer down to special metal pavements of the future. And skirts will fall victim to the wind. Instead ladies' legs will be completely covered in tight fitting silver 'Alcan' foil wrap trousers.

THAT'S LIVES

But it's not all bad news for fellas. These new wind resistant pants will have see-through bottoms.

1000 mph gales lash Britain in year 2000

Traffic jams will be replaced by massive queues in the clouds, as thousands of commuters sail to work – on kites.

PROPELLERS

And satellite dishes on the side of houses will be replaced by windmill style propellers, as greedy home owners cash in on the high winds to provide their own free electricity. Wind speeds exceeding 10,000, miles an hour will provide home owners with 25,000 volts per amp of power – enough electricity to boil a kettle the size of Wembley Stadium – *every three seconds.*

COCKPITS

In the field of sport, world records will be shattered. For example, in the long jump school children will be able to leap 300 yards with ease – more than ten times the present world best. But sports lessons will have to be cancelled, as with their next jump the wind could change and they could be thrown up to a quarter of a mile backwards, through a window or onto a busy main road.

WINGS

Outdoor pop concerts would be impossible, for thousands of Genesis, Dire Straits and Tina Turner fans would be blown away, quite literally. And the noise of a concert being held in Wembley Stadium would wake people up – *in Australia.*

BEATLES

Structural damage caused by high winds will create scenes reminiscent of the Blitz. Insurance claims for

An artist's impression of wind swept Britain in the year 2000.

storm damaged property are already up by 200 per cent on previous figures. But according to the experts, by the year 2000, buildings will collapse like matchwood models, and catch fire spontaneously. Buses and trains will be tossed around like litter, and Britain's streets will be up to ten feet deep in dead bodies. Meanwhile, tidal waves the size of Mount Everest will obliterate our coastline, reducing our island to a blood-soaked paddy field of death.

MONKEES

Plans are already afoot to protect the Royal Family from changes in the weather. By the year 2000 they will have moved into a new, specially designed 'wind sausage' shaped palace. The

new silver, sausage shaped building will swivel on an axis ensuring that it always faces into the wind. And should the weather worsen, the building will turn into a rocket to fly the Royals safely to Mars.

BANANA SPLITS

But the most shocking conclusion arrived at by Government experts is that by the year 2000 humans may no longer rule the world! Man could be forced to take a back seat as evolutionary forces change the face of the planet. Man will have shrunk to a mere 8 inches tall, and could be playing second fiddle to tortoises, which – unaffected by wind due to their streamlined shell – will rule the world.

The new 'sausage shaped' Royal palace of the future nearing completion yesterday.

FEARS OF THE BLUE PETER STARS

We asked a few former Blue Peter presenters to use their knowledge of Blue Peter tortoises and other things to predict what life would be like in the year 2000 if Britain was extremely windy, and ruled by tortoises.

Tennis fan and one-time 'Money Programme' presenter **VALERIE SINGLETON** admitted that she would not be prepared for windy weather.

"I've always hung my washing out on the line, and in high winds that would be virtually impossible", she told us. "A moderate wind would be fine", she added "as that would speed up the drying process."

The late great Ted Moult's Everest double glazing understudy, dog owner and seventies junior TV stunt king **JOHN** 'get down shep' **NOAKES** said that windy weather would be a disaster for him. "I enjoy sailing my yacht around the Mediterranean, and windy weather is bad news for sailors. I'd have to put in to port, and

hope that the tortoise harbour authorities allowed me in", he predicted.

CURRIE - 'Be- spectacled'

ELLIS - 'Pretty'

FREDA - 'Tortoise'

Be-spectacled grin-a-lot former 'Junior Showtime' star **MARK CURRIE** was able to smile, despite our gloomy forecast. "With a name like Currie, I reckon I already know a bit about wind", he quipped light heartedly.

Pretty pregnancy scandal presenter **JANET ELLIS** seemed unsurprised by our horrific weather predictions. "I have noticed it getting a bit windier recently", she remarked. "Perhaps it's something to do with the ozone layer, or Chernobyl", she added speculatively.

Tailors Shop Joke

THE TIE AND THE TROUSERS COMPLIMENT ONE ANOTHER SIR.

OOH, YOU LOOK REALLY SMART TODAY.

THANKS. YOU DON'T LOOK AT ALL BAD YOURSELF

QUEEN MUM'S THE WORD

By our Palace Correspondent

Buckingham Palace officials are today expected to strongly deny rumours that the Queen Mother is to be bundled off into an old people's home.

The rumours came after a woman in Bournemouth reported that the Queen and Prince Phillip had visited her residential care home on the seafront and inspected the facilities.

STAFF

The Royal couple, who used a false name for their visit, were told that the Queen Mum would be one of 32 old folks resident at the home. Staff there would cater for her every need, and her room, which she would share with one other guest, would have a TV, running water and tea making facilities.

TAYLER

According to the home's owner, who prefered not to be named, the Queen and Prince Phillip appeared to be impressed by what they saw. Although the Queen Mother was never mentioned by name, Prince Phillip allegedly referred to "the mother-in-law" on several occasions during the visit, and the couple paid particular attention to the dining room and kitchen facilities.

McGOWAN

"They seemed most anxious that the food was up to scratch", the owner, a woman in her forties, told us. "They said that she'd had trouble in the past with fishbones."

ZETA-JONES

The Queen could expect to pay something between £300 and £500 a week to have her mother put away in a coucil approved home, a considerable financial commitment even for someone of her means. But the advantages would be obvious. Now in her nineties, the

EXCLUSIVE

Queen Mum is believed to talk about nothing but the war, and requires constant attention from Palace staff. Having her put away would relieve a great strain from the already overworked Royal family.

The pressure of living under a shared roof are well known to thousands of families throughout Britain.

ALPHA-SMITH

As one expert put it "It can be a real pain in the arse having some delapidated in-law rambling away in the corner of the room while you're trying to watch something on the telly". As a result every year in Britain over 800,000 senior citizens are put out to pasture, costing the tax payer an incredible £25 billion in social security hand outs.

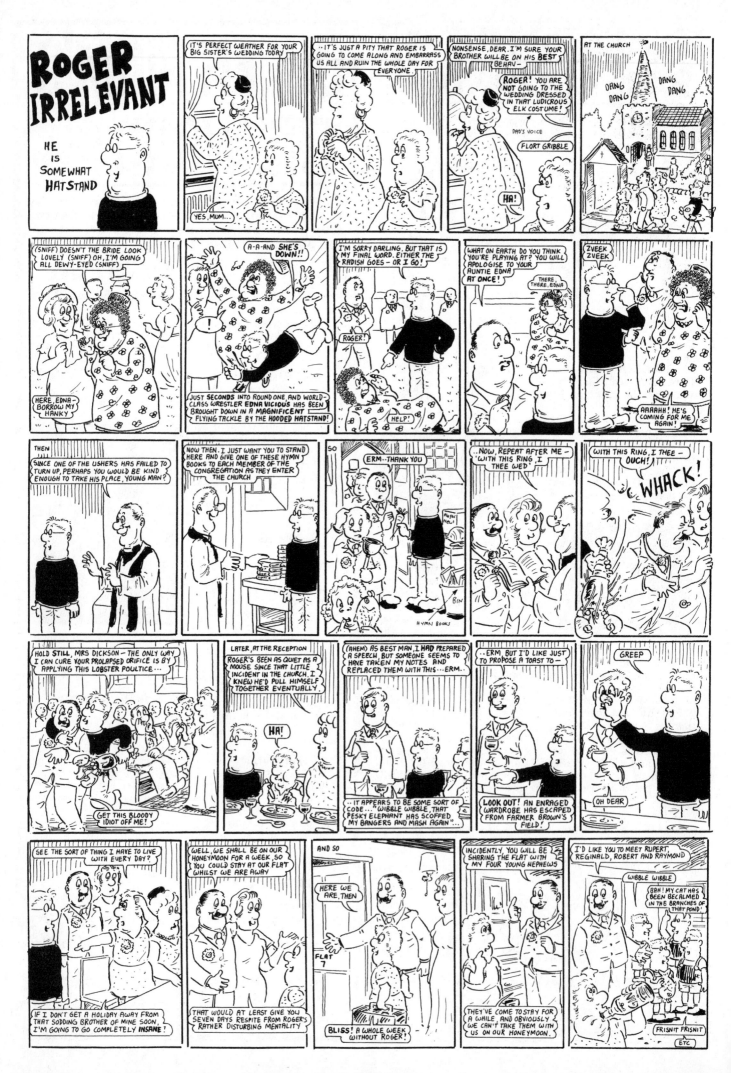

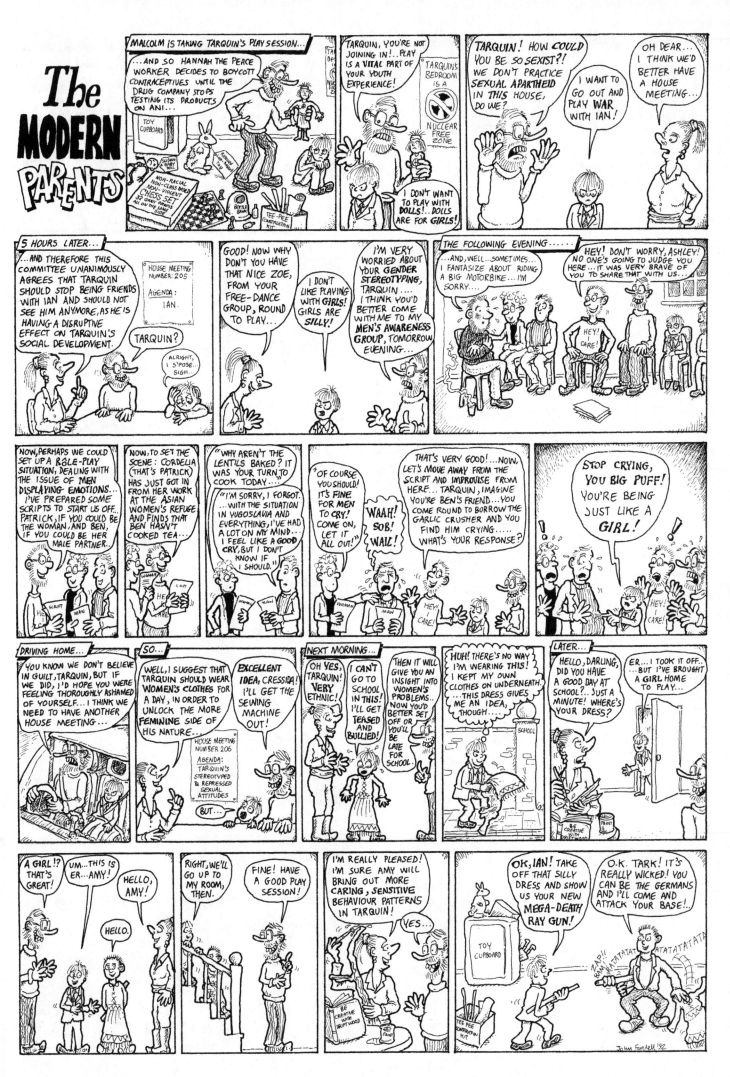

ADVICE ON ICE

Showbiz tips to avoid the slips

Christmas should be a time of fun and laughter, of holly and ivy, of log fires, chestnuts and mistletoe.

But all too often the joy of Christmas turns to tears as dangerous conditions underfoot make the festive season a nightmare for pedestrians.

SLUSH

For every year icy pavements and slush covered pathways cause havoc for hundreds of would-be walkers. And these problems can be complicated by additional hazards, including drifted snow build ups against doorsteps and curbs, irregular mounds of treacherous frozen slush, fresh powdery snow concealing existing layers of ice, and clumsy pensioners sprawling around on the ground in front of you.

FIGHTING

It's every Christmas pedestrian's nightmare. That brief visit to the shops, or casual call on a neighbour, that ends in a fall. And all too often bruised elbows, grazed knees and twisted ankles are the result.

STEEPLE RESTORATION

Of course Christmas is a very busy time of year for the stars of showbusiness, with TV shows, public appearances and pantomime work leaving them more at risk than most when it comes to pedestrian accidents. So we decided to ask **them** what precautions they take, and how they go about reducing the risk of a fall during the inclement winter weather. They certainly have some useful things to say, so why not take a tip from the stars and stay on your feet this Christmas.

Nutty crazy oddball Mr Bean actor comic **ROWAN ATKINSON** knows only too well what it's like to fall on an icy pavement. He's done it several times. His tip is to cut

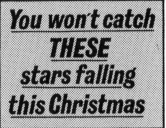
You won't catch THESE stars falling this Christmas

down on Christmas shopping. "Don't buy large or cumbersome presents. Stick to small things like pens and jewelry. Then you can pop them in your pockets and still have both hands free for balancing on your way home".

Comedy actor **ROY BARRACLOUGH**, alias The Street's no-nonsense barmaid Bett Gilroy has learnt his lessons from years spent in panto work across the country. "I've walked on ice, through snow, in slush, and in numerous treacherous combinations of the three", he told us. "I recommend your readers adapt their walking style to suit the conditions. Generally speaking, take shorter steps and raise your feet higher off the ground. A handy hint is to imagine you are wading through water. It works for me."

"Slow down on corners". That was the key advice given by high brow arts commentator **MELVYN BRAGG**. "The vast majority of accidents on ice and snow occur when people are changing direction. So think ahead. Begin to slow down early for a corner, and never hurry. It isn't worth it".

Being a weatherman we thought **MICHAEL FISH** might have some useful advice on how to cope in dangerous walking conditions. And we were right. "Choose the right footwear", he told us. "Wellingtons for snow, something with a good grip for slush, and rubber soled shoes for ice. Also, try bending down, to lower your centre of gravity. Bend your knees, and tilt your head forwards. It may feel uncomfortable, but it works".

Former Holiday show host **CLIFF MICHELMORE** be-

lieves the secret of balance is all in the mind. "In icy conditions our muscles tend to tense up. Our leg movements become jolty and awkward. The answer is to be more relaxed. Think positive. Try skidding a few yards before you start walking. Take a run up and see how far you can slide. Once you've conquered your fear of falling you will then have the confidence to walk normally in these difficult conditions".

Award winning actor and playwright **COLIN WELLAND** admits that walking on slippery and hazardous pavements is one of his worst fears. Indeed, he has been known to stay indoors for months on end in order to avoid walking in nasty weather. "If I do have to go out and there's ice on the ground, I must admit, I chicken out", he confessed. "Rather than walk I just slide along on my bottom, propelling myself with my arms and legs".

This Christmas — Show them you care...

GIVE THEM FAGS

Birds drop 'em for chocolates

AND ALL BECAUSE THE LADIES LOVE...

Chocolates are the key to a woman's pants. So says a new survey published today.

And with Christmas approaching, now is the time for fellas to be buying them. That's the view of Burt Twix, spokesman for the British Association of the National Federation of Chocolate Manufacturers of Great Britain, who commissioned the survey.

HEART

"Traditionally flowers have always been seen as the way to a woman's heart. And that may well still be so. But if you want to get into her knickers, you'd be better off buying chocolates", Mr. Twix told us.

DIAMOND

And he claims that statistics bear him out. "Our survey shows that almost 85% of men who give chocolates get their end away within a couple of days. Whilst out of every hundred men who give flowers, six months later over half of them still haven't even

...it up 'em

had a whiff of action, never mind a leg over".

CLUB

Research carried out in conjunction with the survey revealed another interesting fact about chocolates. "We're still waiting for the final results, but all the signs indicate that chocolates help prevent cancer", he told us.

BRITAIN'S BALLS ARE

Britain's ball makers are having a ball, according to the latest ball figures published today.

Department of Trade statistics show that sales of balls of all types are booming.

GOOD NEWS

And that's good news for High Street ball retailers, who have suffered more than most in the recent recession, with balls sales dropping to an all time low at the beginning of the year.

KING JAMES

But now they're bouncing back, with sales of balls, including foot, golf, basket and beach all on the increase.

BOUNCING BACK

Reg Burton, spokesman for national retail giants World of Balls, told us that ball sales were buoyant throughout Britain. "We stock over 50 balls, everything from medicine to marbles, and they're all rolling off the shelves as fast as we can put them out".

WENDY JAMES

In 1980 a survey revealed that the average man in Britain bought 7 balls, although this figure varied from one individual to another.

HOUSEWIFE'S HUNT HORROR

Horseback toffs tear pet to pieces

A housewife watched in horror as her family pet was torn to shreds by a baying pack of hounds, after fox hunters rode through French windows and into her living room.

Mrs. Eve Froud was sitting watching television in her third floor Putney council maisonette when she was alerted by the sound of hunting horns. Seconds later thirty blood thirsty hounds tore into her living room knocking over furniture, followed by a dozen members of the Putney Hunt on horseback.

BOWL

"The next thing I knew the dogs had somehow pulled my goldfish George out of his bowl, which was on top of the television, and had cornered him behind the settee", Mrs. Froud told us.

BOIL

The horrified housewife then sat and watched helpless as the ferocious hounds tore the tiny fish to shreds, jeered on by the red jacketed hunt members. "I'll never forget George's face as those hounds closed in", Mrs. Froud recalled painfully.

SOIL

Mrs. Froud also alleges that the Master of Hounds, Brigadier Charles Levington Compost-Heap struck her in the face with his riding crop when she tried to intervene, and then shot and killed her husband Dennis, 52, who

No nookie Fry (left) and Blind Date Cilla

was watching television at the time.

SAIL

A spokesman for the Putney Hunt described the incident as 'regrettable', and said that it was not hunt policy to pursue foxes into people's houses. "A formal apology has been made, together with

an offer of compensation for the loss of the goldfish", we were told.

SAID

Members of the Putney Hunt include brainy left wing bonk ban comic Steven Fry, and 'Blind Date' hostess Cilla Black.

WIG WAM BAN

The Queen is on the warpath over plans for a new home being built by Prince Charles in the grounds of Buckingham Palace.

Big Chief Big Ears has gone little plum crazy – and come up with a scheme to build an Indian teepee for himself and his squaw Princess Diana.

FURIOUS

And disgruntled Di is believed to be furious about plans to move her into a tent. Eccentric Charles has always been a big fan of North American red indian culture. But now pale faces at the Palace are seeing red at the redskin Royal's outrageous antics. For the Queen fears that if the building goes ahead, Charles will end up dancing around totem poles in full public view, wearing a red indian outfit.

Already the dotty heir has embarrassed fellow Royals by:
* **INTRODUCING** buffalo into St. James Park.
* **TURNING** up for official engagements carrying a tomahawk, and wearing a full red indian headdress and warpaint.
* **ATTEMPTING** to scalp the King of Norway during an official reception at the Palace.
* **PERFORMING** a rain dance at a Royal garden party, causing the Queen Mother and hundreds of guests to be drenched in the resulting downpour.

Queen has reservations over heap daft plan

But the final straw came when the Queen caught Charles trying to trade the Crown Jewels for a bottle of whisky, two rifles and a top hat.

SIGNALS

Smoke signals from the Palace indicate that following a recent pow wow the Queen issued an ultimatum to her

An artist's impression of Charles o the warpath

raving redskin son. As one insider put it, she told him, "Either stop acting like an indian, or I won't let you be the King". For Charles may be heir to the throne, but the Queen can, at her discretion, give someone else the job if she believes her son is losing his Royal marbles.

IF REDSKIN CHARLIE GETS THE CHOP, WHO'LL FILL HIS MOCCASINS?

Now that Prince Charles has become a red indian, who would YOU like to be the next King or Queen of England?

Why not select your choice from the following list of Regal possibilities. Then, as usual, fill in the coupon and send it to the Queen. Your votes will help her make the final decision – a decision which only she – as the Queen of England – can make.

CHOICE

When making your choice it is important to bear in mind that our future King or Queen must:

* Know which knife and fork to use at a posh do.

* Be able to smile and wave for long periods of time.

* Get on well with old folks and vicars.

* Look good on stamps and money.

Here's a few suggestions to set you thinking. Who would you choose?

BOBBY CHARLTON

With 104 caps for England, top scorer Bobby certainly has good qualifications. 1966 World Cup winner Bobby would make a great ambassador for his country, for unlike certain other former England footballers Bobby has never brought disgrace on his country with allegations of stealing cheap jewellery or shagging someone else's wife in the back of a car.

Pros: World famous celebrity, impeccable reputation, the gentleman of soccer.
Cons: No hair, northern accent, rude brother.

CLIFF RICHARD

The ageless Peter Pan of Pop has represented his country three times in the Eurovision Song Contest – and lost three

times. But Cliff's clean-cut image would be ideal, and his strong Christian faith would stand him in good stead – for if Cliff got the job, King Cliff would be head of the Church of England. But at 56, there must be question marks as to whether Cliff has the means – or the inclination to father a successor.

Pros: Likeable, popular with all age groups, has religion.
Cons: Shadowy past, bachelor boy, starting to look a bit leathery.

ESTHER RANTZEN

Her tireless charity work has made her one of Britain's best loved, big-toothed TV presenters, along with Ken Dodd, Derek Jameson and Janet Street-Porter. Do-gooder Esther is already the consumer Queen of the box, and her Heart of Gold would provide a valuable addition to the Crown Jewels.

Pros: Horsey teeth, posh frocks. Looks the part.
Cons: Obsession with vegetables that look like cocks, and dogs that say "sausages".

JIMMY SAVILLE

One of the Queens closest pals, she Knighted him for his remarkable long running Sunday lunchtime radio show. Famous for his work behind the scenes at Britain's hospitals, and wearing jewellery, and smoking cigars. So owz about you the guys 'n' gals out there, fixing it for Uncle Jim, to be the King. Goodness gracious. Would you believe it. Aughee-aughee-augh!

Pros: Knight, has own jewellery and Rolls Royces (six).
Cons: Wears gold track suits, runs everywhere.

Cut along dotted line

To: The Queen, Buckingh

Dear Queen,
I am very sorry to hear abo
is a red indian but anyway

* *Delete as applicable*

The prospect of an indian chief for King is something the Queen would rather not consider. For if Charles has his way he will probably rule Britain from a wig wam, ride around on a horse (with no saddle) and ambush stage-coaches, while Queen Di would be left carrying her kids around in a papoose. Royal advisors fear such behaviour would be undignified, and would serve only as ammunition for the anti-monarchy lobby, headed by the late Willie Hamilton MP, who is dead.

BABS WINDSOR

Busty Babs would look a picture bursting out of her bra on banknotes – phoaar! And fellas would queue all day at the Post Office (as indeed they already do) to lick her – on stamps. The curvaceous Carry-On Queen wouldn't have far to travel to the Palace – she's a cockney, born and bred. But with a shady ex-husband on the Costa Crime, would the Crown Jewels be safe in her hands?

Pros: Right surname, bubbly personality, big knockers.
Cons: Cockney accent, knockers might pop out during Royal garden parties.

Palace, London.

rince Charles thinking he v that he does I think that

be King/Queen* instead.

Signed _____

MICKEY MOUSE BOUND FOR MIDLANDS
TIPTONDISNEY!

Mickey Mouse millionaire Walt Disney is planning a new multi-million dollar theme park. But it's not going to be built in Tokyo, Texas or Turin. It will be in Tipton, in the West Midlands.

So says property developer Hugo Guthrie. He claims that plans are already well advanced for the breathtaking development – set to be Disney's biggest yet.

WONDERLAND

The 2,000 acre kiddies wonderland will include the world's biggest roller coaster – longer than the London underground and taller than the Post Office tower. There will also be a fairytale castle with fireworks going off behind it, and thousands of real-life Disney favourites including Mickey Mouse, Bugs Bunny, Postman Pat and The Wombles.

ROUNDABOUT

"There will also be a full-size Magic Roundabout, featuring Zebedee, Brian the snail and Mr McGregor, and a Thomas the Tank Engine railway where kiddies can ride on Ivor the Engine and his friends", said Mr. Guthrie, who dreamt up the scheme. And he is convinced that the prestige amusement park will be a big boost for the Tipton area.

CROSSROADS

"*Tiptondisney* will mean big business for the West Midlands, with millions of tourists flocking to see it. We have first class international travel links through Birmingham International airport and now the Channel Tunnel, and we must take full advantage of these", he said.

YELLOW BOX JUNCTION

According to Mr Guthrie the project will need investment from local businesses to get it off the ground, and he is looking to the Recreation and Leisure Committee of Tipton Town Council to set the ball rolling.
"With an initial investment of £300 I could draw up the plans and hire a cement mixer to start preparing the

An artist's impression of the fun park of the future - 'Tiptondisney', drawn by Mr Guthrie's wife, Vera.

site. My brother-in-law is a builder, and once we got started it wouldn't be long before Disney engineers could come in and build *Tiptondisney.*"

GOOD NEWS

So far negotiations between Mr. Guthrie and the Disney Corporation have been restricted to one letter. "I wrote to Walt Disney last year explaining my plans but so far he's not replied. But no news is good news.

BLACK MAGIC

I imagine he's waiting for Tipton Town Council to make the first move before replying, so the ball is in their court. If they give me the £300 it will prove to Mr. Disney that Tipton means business. I just wish they'd put their money where their

Hugo Guthrie - the visionary behind 'Tiptondisney'

mouth is, and *Tiptondisney* could be open by this time next year."

DAIRY BOX

We rang Disney studios in America and asked to speak to Walt Disney, but a receptionist told us that he was unavailable for comment, having been kept in a fridge since dying of lung cancer in 1967.

SOUL ACTS SLAM POLL TAX

Many of the biggest names in soul music have today hit out at the injustice of the Poll Tax.

Top stars, among them Barry White, Lionel Ritchie, Luther Van Dross and Colonel Abrahams have unanimously slammed the injustice of the Tory Government's 'Community Charge' system.

WALRUS

"It's patently unfair", said gravel voiced Barry White, the self proclaimed 'walrus of love', whose string of hits throughout the seventies included 'My Everything'. "Why should a retired couple living in a small cottage have to pay more than a millionaire living in a castle?", asked the 48 stone star.

SEA LION

"Even a return to the old rating system would be better than this poll tax fiasco", blasted Luther Van Dross. And he pointed out the unfairness of the 20% minimum payment. "The tax fails to take into account a person's ability to pay", added a furious Luther.

PENGUIN

Other stars, among them Lionel Ritchie, claim that the Community Charge system of local government finance has proved to be unworkable. "This Tory government has got its sums wrong", he told us. "And to date they have wasted £10 billion of tax payers money trying to enforce a tax which is quite simply uncollectable", said Ritchie, who shot to fame with The Commodores, and whose solo successes include 'Hello' and 'Dancing on the Ceiling'.

CLUB

In the words of his chart hit Colonel Abrahams believes that people living in the higher paid Labour boroughs are 'trapped'.
"Don't you know they're trapped, they're in a cage, they can't get out, they're so confused. And they don't know what to do", he told us yesterday.

Stars unite to fight 'unjust' tax

One person we spoke to believes it's time the talking stopped, and so he has prepared a working paper proposing an alternative system of local government funding. Larry, out of The Floaters, believes a return to the historical 'window tax' is the answer.

UNITED

"The principal is very simple", he told us. "Each household's bill is calculated using the number of windows in the house. Each bill will be based on a standard house with 8 windows, with a set discount per window for less windows up to 4 in total. There will then be a fixed surcharge for extra windows, and an additional 20 per cent levied on double glazing".

CITY

According to Larry, the system will be easy to administer. "Patio doors and french windows will be treated separately, and subject to a standard charge based on a multiple of the normal charge. A greenhouse will be rated the same as two windows. A built-on conservatory, lean-to greenhouse or a glazed porch would count as 3 windows, providing they have a glazed roof and a walled surround not exceeding 2'6" in height (but not less than 18 inches). I'm not exactly sure about dormer windows, skylights and Velux windows – but all internal glazing would be exempt, with the exception, perhaps, of windows in a supporting wall opening into a conservatory, porch or similar lean-to addition. I suppose," the singer told us.

ROVERS

Environment Secretary Michael Heseltine, the man charged with the task of

A soul star yesterday.

Mr Heseltine yesterday.

replacing the Poll Tax, last night claimed that Larry failed to understand the complexities of local government funding, pointing out that a substantial part of it comes from central government. And he labelled his alternative scheme "a ludicrous hotch potch of half-baked ideas".

ROLLS ROYCES

"Larry out of The Floaters would do well to steer clear of politics and stick to singing songs such as 'Float On' ", Mr Heseltine told us yesterday.

IT'S 'BASIN' DONOVAN

Aussie teen pop sensation Jason Donovan is to have a 'basin' haircut. That's the shock news leaked today by showbiz barber Paul, of Chillingham Road, Heaton.

TITS

"I can confirm that Mr Donovan has made an appointment for next Wednesday to have a 'basin' style haircut and singe", said Paul yesterday. The traditional trim, as worn by trendy singer Chris de Burgh, is based on the design of an old fashioned kitchen mop, and was first made popular by The Beatles.

MELONS

"This will be Jason's first visit to my shop", Paul revealed. But in the past a variety of top stars have filed through Paul's modest Newcastle salon. Among them an extra out of Supergran, and in 1965 guitarist Hilton Valentine out of The Animals. "If it wasn't him, it certainly looked a lot like him", said Paul.

KNOCKERS

The good news for pop fans is that they too can have a haircut just like Jason's for only £2.50. "Although Jason books in advance, appointments aren't always necessary, and gentlemen are welcome to call at anytime for a trim, a shave or contraceptives. I'm sure that a good looking lad like Jason will be after a little something for the weekend", quipped Paul.

BRAVE BUD DAVID WINS BATTLE

Top TV comedy actor David Jason, alias Darling Buds star Pop Larkin, has won a desperate two week battle against eczema.

PERFICK

So-brave David, 58, refused to let friends and colleagues in on his tragic secret, hiding

the pain and carrying on with work as usual.

PLONKER

The sudden skin problem struck in 1952, but cleared up a few days later after David's mother bought E45 cream from the chemist.

BUNGLING BT IN PHONE AD BLUNDER

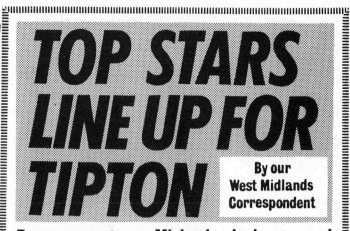

Comedy Jewish telephone actress Maureen Lipman – zany housewife 'Beattie' in the British Telecom ads – has an embarrassing secret to hide. For the star who makes a living telling us to use the phone *doesn't have a phone herself.*

In the £100 million TV ads, Lipman plays a loopy housewife who spends hours ranting to relatives on the phone. And in one she tries to buy a washing machine.

HOODWINKED

The campaign has been a huge hit with the viewers. Telephone sales have more than trebled to £600 billion, and a book based on the TV ads has netted Lipman an estimated £75 million on top of her staggering £250 million fee. Yet we can exclusively reveal that the public have been hoodwinked, for the millionaire actress does without a telephone at her posh North London home.

BULGING

Since Lipman's 'Beattie' character took over the BT ads from yellow comedy tele–phone bird 'Busby' almost ten years ago, Telecom's tills have been bulging, cash registers ringing in massive profits as phone users queue up to imitate their hero 'Beattie' by making calls. But straight faced actress Lipman has probably never picked up a phone in her life. For when we looked in the London telephone directory under 'L', there was no listing under the name of M. Lipman. And now red faced Telecom officials are to consider AXING the £750 million ad campaign.

CHEATED

One disenchanted phone user we spoke to had just paid an £86 Telecom bill. "I feel cheated," she told us. "I think it's a disgrace, and I'll be asking for my money back".

Lipman – alias 'Beattie'.

We wrote to Miss Lipman enclosing a stamped ad–dressed envelope for her comments, but we had received no reply by first post on Thursday. Miss Lipman is married to TV sports commentator Jim Rosenthal.

'FRUIT SEX BABIES' BY YEAR 2000

As controversy continues to rage over the cases of virgin women who wish to have children by artificial means, scientists are now claiming that by the year 2000 it will be possible for men to produce children – by having sex with fruit.

SEX

In a number of experiments carried out to date men are believed to have had sex with fruit, although nothing has happened yet.

TOP STARS LINE UP FOR TIPTON

By our West Midlands Correspondent

Pop megastars Michael Jackson and Madonna have been chosen to spearhead a £5000 campaign to promote Tipton, it was announced yesterday.

Hugo Guthrie, the master-mind behind the campaign, believes that the dynamic and exciting images port-rayed by the stars is just what's needed to put the West Midlands town back on the map.

HEADS

Hugo, a former tourist official, now heads his own PR company, and he has been charged with the task of brightening up Tipton's image for the nineties.

"We want to shake off the old image of a run down, industrial town, and promote the positive side of Tipton, hopefully helping us attract new jobs and invest-ment to the area," Hugo told us.

TAILS

"Michael and Madonna will be helping us to highlight the many investment opportun-ities, grant aid schemes, tax incentives and low rental industrial workshop units available to businesses in the Tipton area. They are the kind of high profile, success-ful figures we want to be associated with Tipton, and I'm sure they will benefit from the relationship too. We have a thriving music industry right here in the West Midlands, with dance halls, record shops and even a recording studio right on our doorstep in nearby Birmingham".

MASSIVE

Already plans are underway for a massive open air concert to launch the fort-night's events, going under the banner of 'Tipton Enterprise Initiative Fort-night'. And both Madonna and Michael Jackson are expected to appear at Tipton

Jackson (above) and Madonna yesterday.

Civic Library to open the 'Tipton Technology' exhibition.

HUGE

In all, the fortnight's events are expected to cost Tipton Borough Council around £5000, but Mr Guthrie is convinced it is money well spent. "Already I've had an enquiry from a waste disposal contractor who is interested in the availability of property in the area", he told us.

ENORMOUS

The exact dates for events are not yet known, as Mr Guthrie is awaiting final confirmation from the stars on the other side of the Atlantic. "I wrote to both of them in America almost a fortnight ago but I've not yet received a reply from either", Mr Guthrie told us yesterday.

T.V. SEX SET TO BOOM

Eurocrats say British aren't getting enough

PHOAAR! Fruity French sit back and enjoy saucy scenes like this every day, while.....

British telly viewers are bottom of the Euro TV sex league, according to officials in Brussels.

Our four major TV channels simply aren't putting enough sex on screen. And EEC bosses in Brussels are set to demand that BBC, ITV and Channel 4 chiefs increase our quota of 'X' certificate action in order to bring us in line with other member nations.

RANDY

Top in the television sex stakes come the randy Italians with their porny politicians and daytime strip shows. And coming a close second are the frisky frogs, who enjoy saucy soap ads and sizzling arty films.

But backward Britain has no nudity before nine, and only occasional glimpses of sex are seen in the odd play by Dennis Potter.

BREASTS

But new rules being drafted in Brussels are set to change all that, with a new fixed Euro-quota of breasts, bottoms and simulated sex having to be broadcast every single night. Exciting changes could be in store for Britain's telly addicts, possibly including:

- **TOPLESS TREATS**
Among your favourite stars popping out each night could be the 'darling buds' of **Catherine Zeta Jones** as she frolics naked in the hay with screen husband Nicholas 'Rodney' Lyndhurst.

Darling Bud Catherine Zeta-Jones and screen hubby Pop 'Plonker' Larkin, alias actor David Jansen.

- **SAUCIER SOAPS**
Raunchy new plots will be written to include full sex between the stars. **Bett Lynch** will be bonking on the bar at the Rovers Return, and in EastEnders, viewers will gasp as **Arthur Fowler** goes all the way with wife Pauline – on the kitchen table.

PEEL

Stroppy slap head **Sinead O'Connor** will be Top of The Pops in 1992 – she'll be the biggest hit of the year if she pops 'em out and shakes 'em about to the sound of her latest record. Meanwhile temperatures will soar as weather girls, including **Trish Williamson,** peel off to reveal their pleasant outlook to boggle eyed viewers, reading the weather in saucy half cupped leather bras and revealing elasticated thongs.

PIPS

And wives wouldn't mind hubby tuning in to the football quite so much if **Jimmy Hill** analysed games in the altogether! If Jimmy's strapping chin is anything to go by, the girls would have plenty to get excited about as the game got underway.

SUPREMES

The BBC's news and current affairs programmes, renowned throughout the world for being dull and boring, would be revolutionised. 'Newsnight' would become *Nudesnight* as **Jeremy Paxman** and company replaced sober suits with birthday suits.

KIEVS

And instead of reviewing the morning papers at the end of each show, the programme would finish with a huge on-screen sex session. Guests, including Cabinet Ministers and top MPs such as **Norman Lamont, Kenneth Baker, Neil**

WAHEY! Spawney Ities get a load of this lot - 24 hour tits on every TV screen.

ZZZZZ! Meanwhile in boring Britain viewers regularly fall asleep to scenes like this.

Kinnock and **Clare Short,** will all be encouraged to fondle their own sexual organs and explore each other's bodies, while the show's hosts perform simulated homosexual acts on a large pink waterbed. Or something like that.

TIKKAS

People we spoke to on the streets yesterday gave a big thumbs up to plans for sexier TV. "I think it will be great seeing everybody's tits on the telly", Bob Smith of Fulchester told us.
However TV watchdogs including Mary Whitehouse need not worry. It won't be a question of 'anything goes'. Responsible TV chiefs will step in to draw the line. "It will still be a case of strictly no flapshots, popshots or panhandles", as one TV insider put it this afternoon.

EX~ STING ~CT

Pop star Sting is hoping to get across a serious message to fans.
And the message is "If dinosaurs aren't extinct already – and they very probably are – at the rate man is going they definitely will be soon".

DINOSAURS

Conservationist Sting, who's hits include 'My Bed's Too Big' and 'Walking on the Moon', admits that in all likelyhood dinosaurs *are* already extinct. But he also conceeds that there is a very slim chance examples of the prehistoric giants may still survive in remote corners of the Earth, as yet untouched by man.

AFRICA

"There might still be some left on a lost plateau or secret valley somewhere in Africa, or something", the millionaire singer and actor told us.

STING - Worried about dinosaurs

But the Newcastle born former milkman fears that *if* there are still any dinosaurs left (even though he knows there probably aren't) – but *if* there are, then they *will* soon be extinct.

EXTINCT

"If we continue to waste the planet Earth's resources the way we are doing today, then any dinosaurs that *are* left, will be extinct – probably by the year 2000", said the singer.

UNLIKELY

"I know its really, *really* unlikely that there are any left, but all I'm saying is that *if* there are – and just imagine if there were – then there *definitely won't be*, soon", he added.

Meet Britain's only real life
GHOSTBUSTER!

Most people wouldn't dream of spending the night in a haunted house. But Bob Smithers does it all the time. In fact, he does it for a living!

Bob is Britain's only full-time ghostbuster, and rather than running away from them, he's been chasing ghoulish guests out of haunted houses for the last twenty years.

ICE CREAM

Bob, who is 42, began his unusual career purely by accident. An ice cream man by trade, late one evening he stopped his van to sell an ice cream to a young soldier standing at the roadside.
"He was a young man – about 18, and he asked me for a '99' with rasberry sauce on it", Bob clearly recalls. "I went to put the ice cream in the cone, but when I turned back he had vanished".

SOLDIER

"A few days later I spotted a newspaper and on the front was a picture of the soldier. It said he had been killed in the war – thirty years earlier. I immediately drove back along the road to the spot where he had been standing, and sure enough, he still wasn't there".

BLUE

From that moment on Bob was hooked, and he has been ghost hunting ever since. Advertising mainly in post office windows, he is on 24-hour call to come and deal with ghosts all over the country.

Ghostly find - the soldiers head that Bob found on a bus stop.

"Most of my calls come late at night", he told us "as ghosts are at their busiest in the dark. But contrary to popular belief, real life ghost hunting can be a pretty boring business. People tend to imagine ghosts walking through walls, carrying their head under one arm, or dragging chains around behind them. But it's nothing like that.

DARK

Nine times out of ten you don't even see the ghost – a lot of them are invisible nowadays. And most of the ghosts I do see are just sort of green clouds of energy that float about and shine in the dark. In fact you can get a nasty shock if you touch one of those".

STAR

Hollywood movie makers paint a more exciting picture of the supernatural. And ironically, it's Bob they usually come to for advice. "One day they came to me with the script for the film Poltergeist. It was all about a ghost that lived in a house, and Tom Cruise was going to play it, wearing a blanket on his head. To make him sound a bit more scary they were going to make him talk through a plastic drainpipe. I told them to forget it – it simply wasn't scary enough.

A Hollywood actor similar to 'not scary' Tom Cruise.

The previous week I'd exercised a ghost that had been living in a cupboard, so I suggested that in the film the ghost should live in a cupboard or a telly or something. They thought it was a great idea, and the film went on to be a great hit. All thanks to my knowledge about ghosts.

UNUSUAL

"The most unusual place I ever had to exercize a ghost from was a bus stop. This particular bus stop had been haunted for many years by a headless soldier who every night used to sit and wait for the last bus. The drivers were so scared they refused to stop there, and as a result intending passengers had to walk to the next stop – several hundred yards away.

HOME

Anyway, there's always a reason for ghosts, so what I usually do is go to the library to do research and find out about them. Sure enough in an old newspaper I read about an accident at the very same bus stop over 100 years ago. A young soldier had been knocked over and killed running to catch the last bus home. His head had never been found.

Bob on his way to bust a ghost

That evening I sat at the bus stop, and sure enough I could feel a presence next to me. Then I got to thinking about the missing head. That was probably why the soldier's spirit was not at rest – because his head was missing.

PUPPETEER

I looked around for a few moments then thought to myself, 'I bet they never checked on top of the bus stop'. Sure enough, I climbed up and there it was – a dusty skull covered in cobwebs, and still wearing an army hat. It must have laid there for over 100 years. I took the skull to a nearby cemetery and buried it in a hole, then I said some prayers. As I prayed I could feel that soldier's presence. It was as if he was standing next to me, saying "Thank-you for burying my head".

INDUSTRY

Bob is loathe to divulge the secrets of his trade, although he admits that ghost busting today is a high tech industry.

'If you've got a ghost, I'm your man' says Bob

"I don't use any onions, or wooden steaks like they do in the movies", he laughed. "My main tool is my ghost-o-meter. You can't buy them in the shops – you have to make them yourself. You've got to be a bit of an engineer in this game, I can tell you."

TRANSPORT

Bob described his ghost-o-meter as a cross between a torch and a walking stick, with a coat hanger on the end, and he uses it to detect ghosts. "It only works in the dark", he told us "and it takes six batteries – which don't usually last very long", he added.

EDUCATION

Indeed ghost busting is an expensive business. The high powered batteries cost almost £3 for a pack of six, and on top of that Bob has his petrol to pay for. "The cost of my petrol varies from job to job, depending on how far I have to travel to get there", said Bob, who drives a scooter. "Motorised transport is essential, as I get calls from all over the country, and you can't always get a bus, especially at weekends".

SOCIAL SECURITY

Despite thousands of nights spent in haunted houses, castles and mansions, Bob inistsits that he's never once been scared. But there have been occasions when he's given one or two other people a fright.
"I'll never forget the time I was looking for a ghost in a church graveyard. It was really spooky, with bats everywhere, and it was a full moon. It was Christmas Eve

so I'd had a few drinks, and before I knew it I'd nodded off to sleep. While I was asleep I must have rolled over and fallen into a freshly dug grave, because when I awoke I'd been buried – the grave digger had filled it in!

SERVICE

So anyway, there was me digging away trying to get out of this grave. Meanwhile the Christmas morning church service had just ended and all the congregation we're coming out – just in time to see yours truly appear from out of the grave!

M.O.T.

I was all covered in soil, I had a nosebleed and the worms had ate my clothes so I looked just like a zombie! You should have seen their faces! Did they shit them-selves or what?!
Next week: How Bob was seduced by teenage lesbian vampires – with pictures.

STARS ON MARS

Many of today's top stars share an unusual ambition – to fly to Mars on a space ship.

For as science edges man ever closer to the mysterious red planet, the possibility of commercial space flights to the planet Mars looms larger.

SHUTTLE

Indeed, many space experts believe a regular shuttle service could come into effect within a few years or so.

RACQUET

In America, speculative travel agents are cashing in early, and are already taking bookings for the space journey of a lifetime. But would-be space travellers are warned – prices look set to rocket beyond the budget of most holiday makers. *For a single return journey could cost as much as a million pounds*. And with prices like that, it is only the rich and famous who are buying.

BAT

Already booked up are many of the biggest names in Hollywood, among them Jack Nicholson, Dustin Hoffman, Gregory Peck and Julie Andrews. And other stars set to scramble for stand-by tickets include Michelle Pieffer, Bruce Springsteen and Barry Manilow.

SPIDER

Indeed, Manilow, America's richest man, has already commissioned the first holiday home in space. Top scientists are studying his plans for a 12 bedroom mansion on Mars, and providing technical problems can be overcome, building work will begin by the end of the year.

SUPER

Many disappointed stars have been turned away from travel agents, and are trying to obtain tickets on the black market. Hollywood touts are rumoured to be charging over *£50 million* for a third class single ticket – and stars like Burt Reynolds are snapping them up. For tough guy Burt was originally refused a ticket by travel agents who feared that his wig would come off in space.

GREEN CROSS

One lucky celebrity who will not be paying over the odds

Celebrities queue for journey into space

Gregory Peck and Charlton Heston (above) prepare for a trip to Mars under test conditions at N.A.S.A.'s Kennedy Space Centre. (Below) Burt Reynolds - wig worry.

for his journey to Mars is Star Trek actor James Kirk. Travel officials have offered him a **FREE** return journey to Mars as guest of honour, and Kirk will ceremonially launch the first flight by pressing the start button on the space ship's flight deck.

MORSE

British stars have given a cool reception to news of possible space flights, with only a handful of enquiries being received from this side of the Atlantic. However, singer Tom Jones may well pip the Americans in the celebrity space race. For Welshman Tom has ploughed profits from his singing career into his own space ship, which he hopes to launch this spring. "It's more of a hobby than anything else", modest Tom told us. "I'll be happy if I can get as far as the moon".

LeTTeRBox

LETTERBOCKS VIZ COMIC P.O. BOX 1PT NEWCASTLE-UPON-TYNE NE 99 1PT

T.V. Burt ad's a gas, man

I must admit I was never a fan of British Gas. But all that changed when I saw their brilliant TV ad featuring Burt Reynolds. Ever since I've done all my cooking with gas.

Of course prior to that I'd run my fucking gas cooker with Duracell batteries.

B. Jones
Biddlecombe

On the subject of ginger hair (S. Dressing's letter, Viz 50), I'm not sure, but I think they've got something wrong with their eyeballs as well. Have any other readers noticed this?

I. Marsh
Careworthy

I sometimes think the manager of my building society must be ginger. Either that or he's Welsh. The daft bastard was only too pleased to lend me the £100,000 I needed to buy a flat, despite the fact that it was only worth £50,000! Now he says he wants his money back. Well, as far as I'm concerned he can whistle out his arse for it.

K. Rowland
London

Am I mistaken, or has everyone from Manchester got a bloody ridiculous haircut?

P. Squalls
Bristol

Call time on the law

Off duty police officers should be banned from entering pubs or other licensed premises. They should be setting an example to young people, not encouraging them to go out and get drunk.

Mrs. K. Lewis
Ormsby

I am going blind. How about a quick picture of Disneyland?

A. McMahon
Tewsbury

Sorry Mr. McMahon. We can't find one.

I am heartily sick of the peurile abuse being hurled at ginger haired people through the pages of your magazine. Just because we have no obvious eyebrows, are bad tempered and can't go outside if the sun is shining doesn't make us any different from everyone else.

Come on Viz. Give the reds a rest!

I. M. Rusty
Redhill

After watching a recent harrowing episode of 'Watchdog' my husband clambered into our Hotpoint washing machine and has steadfastly refused to come out ever since. He took with him a bottle of whisky and a packet of twenty Rothmans, and has been amusing himself by playing the guitar. It is now over three weeks since I have been able to use the machine. Clearly my husband must bear some responsibility for his own foolish behaviour, but surely it is irresponsible of a programme such as 'Watchdog' to put ideas like this into people's heads.

Doris Ranged
Chaldon, Surrey

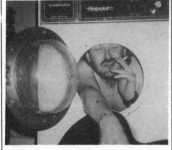

I don't think the police should be allowed to play football. By running around in short trousers chasing after a football they leave themselves wide open to ridicule. It's no wonder children no longer respect the British bobby if this is how they behave in their spare time.

Mrs. K. Lewis
Ormsby

It's the page that puts the 'Christ' back into Xmas

Television companies take note

I have reluctantly come to accept that swearing on television is now a fact of life. But surely with the technology available today the TV companies could provide viewers with some sort of warning of approaching bad language. I have a large, old fashioned car horn which I keep under my chair to scare burglars. If a five second countdown was to appear on the bottom corner of the screen warning of an approaching obscenity, this would give me ample time to sound my horn in order to drown out the offending word.

Come on TV companies. It's worth thinking about.

Mrs. P. Thorburn
Haddington

I am a butcher, and the letters of my name can be rearranged to spell 'MY JOB IS TO SELL MEAT'. Can any of your readers beat that?

Tommy Jobisselleat
Oakhampton

'Classical' music is just shit

I'm sick of all these people who pretend to like 'classical' music. The problem has got so bad that record stores now devote entire departments to this rubbish. Let's face it. The only reason anyone buys these awful records is to try and impress high class birds. Well I'm a high class bird, and I think they're all queers.

Claudia D'Arcy-Desforges
Holland Park

Doesn't the Queen Mum look marvellous for her age. I am currently trying to imitate her radiant looks and lovely smile by painting my teeth yellow and sleeping with my face immersed in vinegar. Does anyone know where I can buy a silly hat?

J. Devine
Edgware

I think it wrong that police officers should be allowed to take part in TV game shows such as 'Every Second Counts' and 'Catchphrase'. It would be both undignified and embarrassing if they were to get a question wrong, and public respect for the police force would be lost.

Mrs. K. Lewis
Ormsby

Don't talk such rot

Who says sugar rots your teeth? This is just another example of scaremongering by greedy dentists desperate to sell us toothpaste. I'm going to keep on eating as much sugar as I jolly well like, and if any dentist tries to stop me I'll punch his bloody lights out, so help me.

Albert Johnson
Lambeth

What Nanette Newman doesn't tell you is that with the amount of money you need to buy a bottle of Fairy bloody Liquid you could almost pay for a meal out in a restaurant. And then someone else does the dishes for you.

B. Jones
Biddlecombe

An insurance form asked whether I have any valuable antiques in my house. "Only you, eh dear?" I joked with my wife. She's 96, and her gold teeth are probably worth more than our entire house contents. Luckily she didn't hear my remark. She's as deaf as a post.

D. P. Course
Evesham

Having nothing to say is no excuse for not writing to Letterbox. Just look at the kind of dross we publish. So come on readers, put pen to paper. Don't delay, write today. It's your chance to have a say etc. etc. etc.

«TOP TIPS»

INJECT food colouring into the bottom of your toothpaste tube using a hypodermic needle. When the toothpaste appears coloured, you will know it's time to buy a new tube.

G. Duckworth
Barnsley

PRETEND that your house is a 'Bed & Breakfast' establishment by ordering an extra 50 pints of milk each day, and placing a 'Bed & Breakfast' sign in your front window. Unwanted callers can easily be dissuaded by adding a simple 'No Vacancies' sign.

A. Conway
Dundee

LOOK extra hard on long train journeys by saving all your empty beer cans for a week and lining them up on the table in front of you.

Tugger Trotman
Wirral

HANG Brussels sprouts on the end of a piece of string. Hey presto! Edible Christmas decorations for the kids.

Mrs. I. Jones
Hebden Bridge

GOLFERS! empty egg boxes make ideal containers for your golf balls. Except that they're a little bit too small.

A. Simmons
Cheltenham

RAILWAY commuters. When boarding your train attach a length of rope to the carriage door, and tie the other end firmly around your ankle. In the event of a train crash by following the rope you will be able to find your way out of the wreckage in the dark.

Dave Parsnip
Altringham

A CORK dangling from the end of a long stick can be used to chase flies harmlessly out the window.

Mrs. Doris Peterson
Rhyll

A STRING of sausages draped across the room makes an ideal edible Christmas decoration. But be sure to cook them before giving them to the kids.

Mrs. I. Jones
Hebden Bridge

DON'T invite drug addicts round for a meal on Boxing Day. They may find the offer of 'cold turkey' embarrassing or offensive.

Steven Howlett
London N8

KEEP the seat next to you on the train vacant by smiling and nodding at people as they walk up the aisle.

Mrs. Deidre Partridge
Rugby

GLUE desiccated coconut to your windows this Christmas for a perfect 'snow' effect. Afterwards it can be chiseled off and fried – a perfect treat for the kids.

Mrs. I. Jones
Hebden Bridge

BRIDES! Take no risks on your big day. Place marshmallows under your wedding cake to help it withstand any minor earthquakes or tremors.

D. Puttnam
Ryhope

TAKE a leaf out of the skateboarder's book this winter. Strap empty egg boxes to your knees and elbows to prevent injury when falling on ice.

G. Hall
Motherwell

WHEN it's your round, carry all the drinks back from the bar by covering them with clingfilm and putting them in your pockets.

D. Porter
Rochester

PINEAPPLE rings make attractive tree decorations – and slot easily onto the branches of your tree.

Mrs. I. Jones
Hebden Bridge

LUNCHBOX JURY

This week:
BRIAN CLOUGH

Each week we summon you, the readers, to serve on our Lunchbox Jury. This week we are preparing a packed lunch for controversial football manager **Brian Clough**, and we want you, the members of the Lunchbox Jury, to decide which of the lunchboxes listed below will be best for Brian.

BRIAN

Consider carefully the evidence before you. Brian is 58, but remains an active sportsman. He starts his day with a big breakfast, before a busy morning spent coaching his Nottingham Forest players. Brian then gets involved in stressful office work in the afternoon, and must wait until 7 pm for his next main meal. Outspoken Brian has a sweet tooth, but his wife is a little concerned about his waistline.

Mr McHENRY

Now retire, and consider your verdict. Then complete the coupon below, indicating which lunch you feel would be most suitable. Send your votes to the address on the form, and whichever lunchbox receives the most votes will be packed and posted to Brian.

To: The Foreman, Lunchbox Jury, Viz, P.O. Box 1PT, Newcastle upon Tyne NE99 1PT.

In the case of Brian Clough's lunchbox, I vote for the following. (Tick one only).

Lunchbox No. 1 ☐

6 Ham, cheese & pickle sandwiches on white bread.
A pork pie.
A Scotch egg.
A slice of date and walnut cake.
A flask of tea.

Lunchbox No. 2 ☐

4 peanut butter sandwiches on white bread.
A Burton's Waggon Wheel.
2 packets of prawn cocktail crisps.
An individual fruit pie.
A tin of Appletise.

Lunchbox No. 3 ☐

2 slices of Riveta crispbread with cream cheese and pineapple.
An apple.
A carton of natural yoghurt.

Lunchbox No. 4 ☐

1 tuna mayonnaise sandwich on brown bread.
1 packet of plain crisps.
1 vegetable samosa.
1 carton of Ribena.
1 Tunnock's Caramel Wafer.

Lunchbox No. 5 ☐

4 thick cut cheese and onion sandwiches.
1 mince and onion pie.
A large sausage roll.
A snack size Kit Kat.

Lunchbox No. 6 ☐

2 chicken sandwiches.
1 cheese and onion pasty.
1 Bakewell tart.
1 can of lemonade.
1 finger of fudge.

"Daddy — I've done a poo-poo"

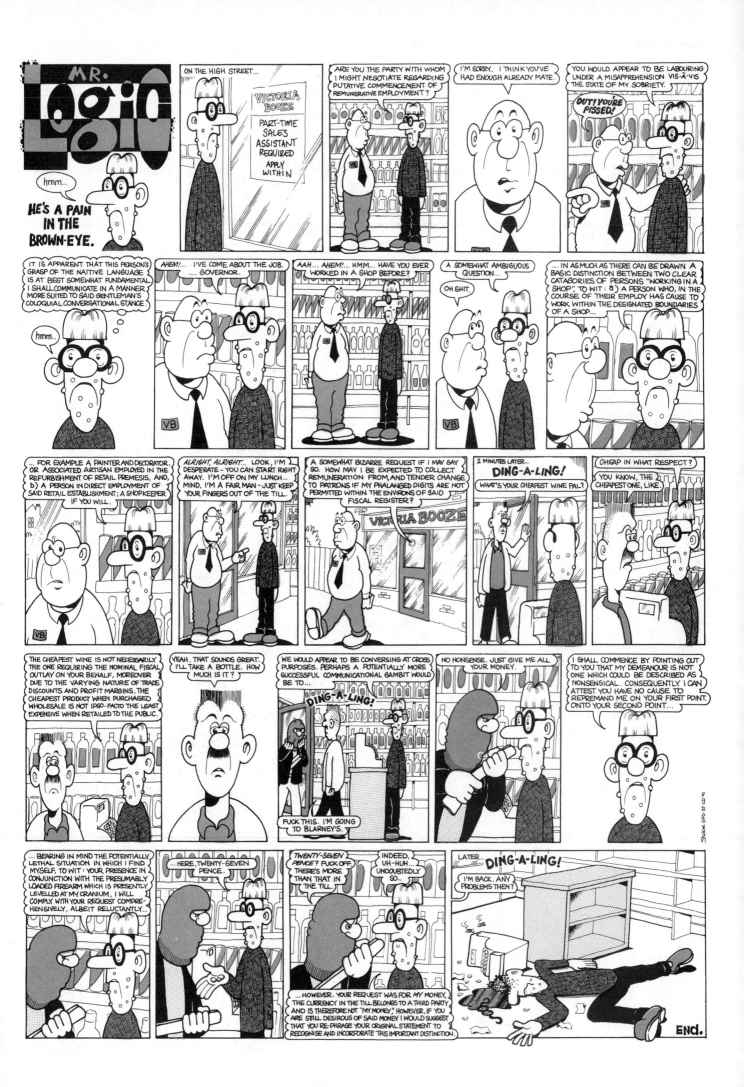

102

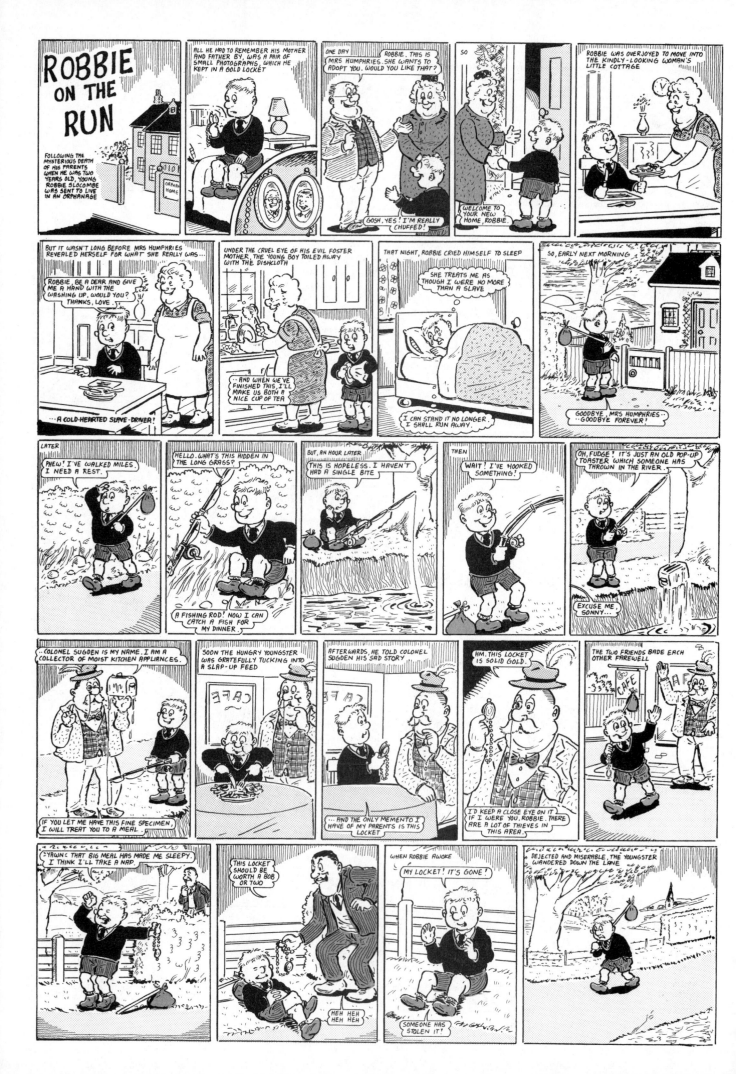

Let's play CELEBRITY WHOREHOUSE

'A bit of harmless fun with the stars'

A: FOR A GOOD TIME RING **JUDI**
B: FOR A GOOD TIME RING **VIKKI**
C: FOR A GOOD TIME RING **IVY**
D: FOR A GOOD TIME RING **KIM**
E: FOR A GOOD TIME RING **KYLIE**
F: FOR A GOOD TIME RING **JEANETTE**

It's hard to imagine our top TV celebrities like Melvyn Bragg kerb crawling in Kings Cross. And It's even harder to imagine famous female stars like actress Dame Judi Dench touting for business on a street corner dressed in a revealing short skirt and stockings.

But that's exactly what we've done. We call it Celebrity Whorehouse, and it's a game you can play along with. And for the winner there'll be a chance to sleep with **YOUR** favourite star, or a fifty pounds cash prize.

HARMLESS

Of course it would be ridiculous to suggest that any celebrity would act either as a prostitute or as a client. And not for one moment would we do so. But just for fun, we've *imagined* that six female celebrities are 'on the game', and that six male showbiz stars are looking for a good time. It's a fairly futile and pointless exercise, but it helps fill the magazine.

FUN

To play the game we want you to guess how much each of the celebrity clients would be prepared to pay to go 'all the way' (that is to have *full sex*) with each of the celebrity whores. For example if, just for fun, you thought Rolf Harris would fork out fifty quid to have sex with fellow Aussie Kylie Minogue, enter '£50' in box 'E' against Rolf's picture, etc. Simple, isn't it?

Send your completed forms to 'Celebrity Whorehouse Competition', Viz, P.O. Box 1PT, Newcastle upon Tyne, NE99 1PT. Please write on the back of your envelope the name of the Celebrity with whom you'd most like to have sex.

JIM DAVIDSON
WOULD PAY...

A	B	C
D	E	F

M. C. HAMMER
WOULD PAY...

A	B	C
D	E	F

ROLF HARRIS
WOULD PAY...

A	B	C
D	E	F

MELVYN BRAGG
WOULD PAY...

A	B	C
D	E	F

IAN McCASKILL
WOULD PAY...

A	B	C
D	E	F

SIR A. BURNETT
WOULD PAY...

A	B	C
D	E	F

Celebrity Pimp

Each week, just for fun, we select a top celebrity from the world of telly, sport and entertainment to act as our **Celebrity Pimp.** We invite him to cruise the streets in a pink cadillac and floppy hat, and we imagine which three Celebrity Whores he would choose to act as his 'bitches'.

Needless to say, there is no implication whatsoever that any of the celebrities named would act in the way we have described. This is all just for fun.

This week we've chosen former England footballer and TV soccer analyst **TREVOR BROOKING** as our Celebrity Pimp, and we've tried to imagine which three well known women Trevor might choose to act as his prostitutes. Looks aren't everything, so we've selected Eastenders'

Michelle Fowler as Trevor's first girl. Her tough, streetwise background would be an asset to any pimp.

A good head for figures is essential for any prostitute, especially when it comes to handing over her pimp's share of the money! If any of his bitches short-changed Trevor, they could be in big trouble. For this reason we think Countdown's **Carol Vorderman** would be a worthy addition to Trevor's vice racket. Lastly, we've chosen the Media Show's **Emma Freud,** because we fancy her.

Next Week: Celebrity Drug Dealer, where top stars battle it out in a 'Manchester style' drug war.

106

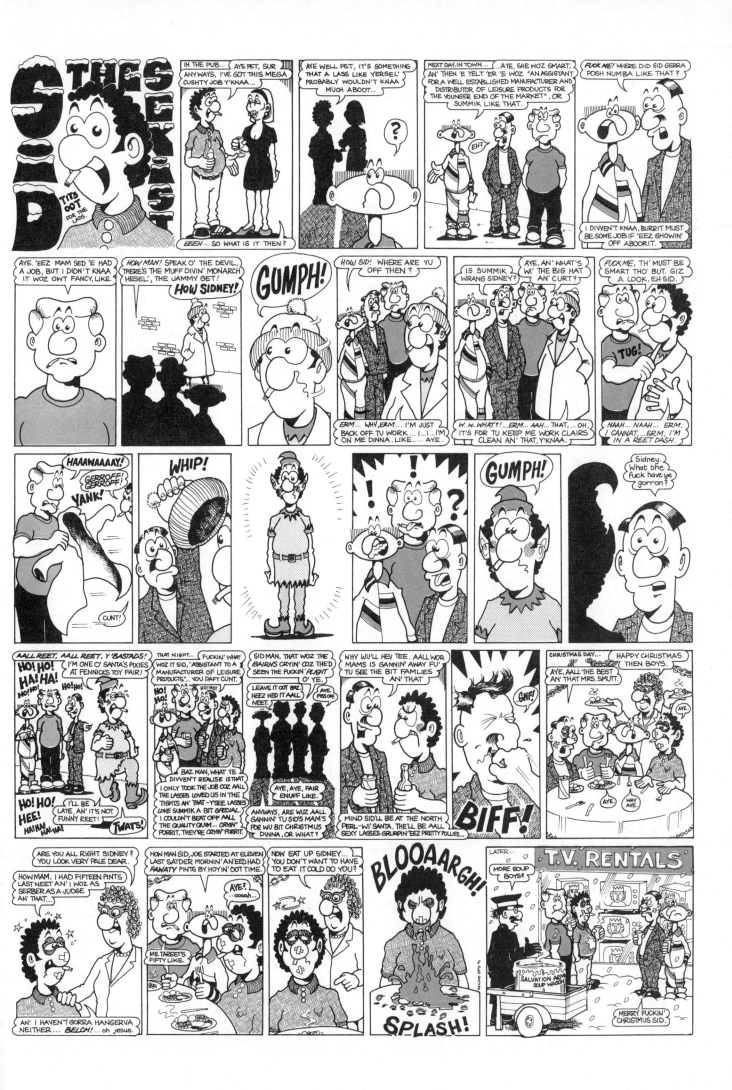

CD 1.92 Photography by Colin Davison

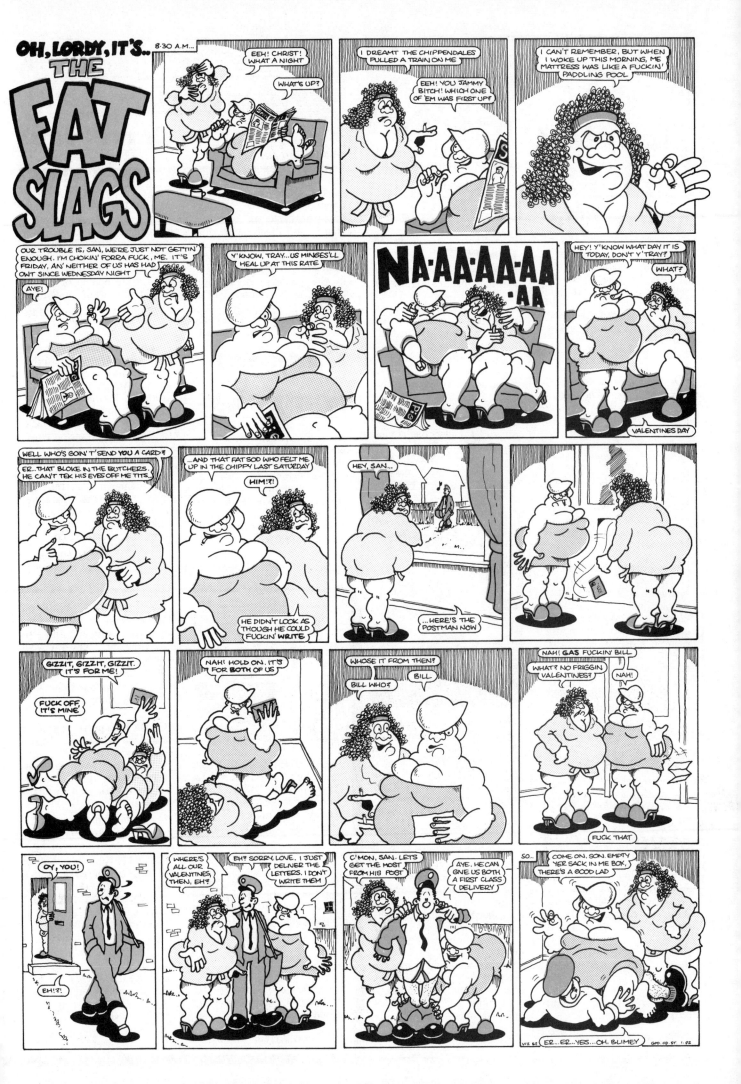

Letterbox

Happiest days of your life

Looking back on my school-days I fondly remember the carefree life I lead, and the naive optimism that all young children shared. I also seem to recall that the female P.E. teachers were always lesbians.

Mr F. Hunt
Colchester

Do you have lasting memories of your school-days? Choking on your first cigarette behind the bike sheds, having your teeth kicked out by the school bully, or improper sexual advances made to you by members of the teaching staff. If so, why not share them with us. Write to Letterbox, and remember to mark your envelope 'School Memories'.

I have a simple remedy to the problem of our overcrowded motorways. Why not allow people in the upper tax bracket only to drive in the outside lane. And during the rush hour drivers who's cars are more than five years old would have to pull in onto the hard shoulder. The problem of congestion would be cured at a single stroke.

H. Balderston-Smythe
Newmarket

Mix up between two Noels

Last Saturday I waited with excitement for the new TV programme 'Noel's House Party' to begin. Imagine my disappointment to find that the show was presented by Noel Edmunds, not Noel Burke, lead singer of the re-formed 'Echo and the Bunnymen'. I wish the BBC would be more specific in future.

I. McGregor
Liverpool

Letterbocks
Viz Commick
P.O. Box 1 PT
Newcasle upon Tyne
NE99 1PT

On the subject of people in washing machines, (Mrs D. Ranged's letter, Viz 51), it came as a great relief to know that other people share the same problem. My husband has also become trapped in a Hotpoint washing machine as a result of watching the 'Watchdog' TV programme, and interferes with my housework by playing the guitar loudly all day. Have any other readers had similar problems with this model?

V. Sarson (Mrs)
Caterham

Has anyone else taken a photo of their husband with his head sticking out of a washing machine, holding a guitar? If so, send them to our usual address. We'll pay £5 for everyone we publish, except the two we've already used.

Now that they've got rid of the Poll Tax, isn't it about time the Government got rid of this ridiculous so-called 'decimalised currency'. Surely after twenty years of monetary mayhem the people at the Treasury must realise it simply isn't going to work.
Mr Major would earn the respect of a great many people if he backed down gracefully, and brought back the old money.

Mrs U. Hurst
Dewhurst

It is a little known fact, that by law, motorists may only go around roundabouts *three* times before taking an exit. Would it not be an idea to solve the problem of youth unemployment by making youngsters sit on roundabouts and look out for anyone violating this rule. If, say, four youths were posted on every roundabout in the country, unemployment could be eliminated at a stroke.

H. Balderston-Smythe
Newmarket

Keep fat campaign

As a fat person who eats lardy food all day while sitting watching television, I find it most encouraging that 'keep-fit' athletics commentator Ron Pickering is dead, while Cyril Smith is alive. So much for so-called 'healthy lifestyles'.

F. Styles
Preston

Carrot top's comic upset

My brother, who has ginger hair, is a big fan of your comic. However he was extremely upset after reading the cruel and hurtful things you said about ginger people. As a result neither of us will be buying your magazine again.

M. Pitt
Gloucester

I am the Headmaster of Cambridge University and I am therefore very intelligent and I would like to congratulate Viz readers on the compassionate, erudite and constructive way in which the Letterbox debate on ginger hair has been conducted. It is of course a scientific fact that ginger haired people are less intelligent than the rest of us, and I would therefore ignore totally any hollow and childish criticisms levelled by them at your magazine.

The Headmaster
Cambridge University

Top tips

NOW is the time to freeze petrol and store it in the ice tray of your fridge. Come summer these handy 'petrol cubes' will help cool your engine as you drive along.

B. Baxter
Potters Bar

GARDENERS. Save yourself the trouble of re-potting plants by planting them in a big enough pot in the first place.

P. Mandeville
Marlborough

MAKE firelighters by steeping white nougat overnight in petrol.

B. Baxter
Potters Bar

TV VIEWERS. Avoid the frustration of losing your remote control unit by keeping it in a 'cowboy' style holster fashioned out of a child's sock and an old belt.

Mike Thornton
Jesmond

CREATE a perfect pond for small gardens by burying an old saucepan and filling it with water. Add an up-turned soda siphon and hey presto – an ornamental fountain.

G. Wilmot
Edmundbuyers

CREATE your own 'boil in the bag' cod in parsley sauce by scraping the bread-crumbs off a fish finger and placing it inside a used condom.

E. Evans
Evesham

SMOKERS. Wear a golf visor between your nose and top lip to keep your cigarette dry in the shower.

D. Quigley
Rotherham

By continually knocking teachers, you only make yourselves look stupid an uninformed. A recent letter implied that teachers were overpaid. Well I am a teacher, and have been for twenty-five years, and I can assure you that it is *not* possible to survive on a teacher's wage. Fortunately, teacher's hours are so short I am able to hold down another full-time job – working in an office.

K. Smith
Bolton

A schoolteacher yesterday

It seems ridiculous to waste the police's time by expecting them to catch speeding motorists. I'm sure they have far better things to do. Why not replace traffic police with a simple 'honesty box' situated on every car's dashboard. Motorists could then pay 10p every time they exceed the speed limit, and a pound if they do more than 100 miles per hour.

The system could also be used to penalise slower drivers who get in other people's way. They could pay an extra 50p every time they are overtaken.

H. Balderston-Smythe
Newmarket

I'm not one to gossip

I'm not one to gossip, but my next door neighbour has ginger hair, and he's just been convicted of driving without due care and attention.

Mrs S. Varson
Surrey

They say crime doesn't pay. Well I wouldn't know. At the minute I've been locked up for something I didn't do. But it's Sod's Law really. They never caught me on the five occasions when I did actually do something.

KV0795 Timlett
H.M.P. Feltham
Bedford Road
Feltham
Middx TW13 4ND
P.S. Does anyone want to write to me?

SMUGGLE whisky out of the house by pouring it down the sink and collecting it in a saucepan under the drainpipe.

Steven Pearlman
Soapdish

DON'T throw out left over chips. Leave them in a shoebox in the freezer, and three months later heat them up in the microwave. Hey presto – exciting American French fries!

Mrs Daisy Pengelly
Redruth

LEAVE your lights on whenever you park your car in a large car park. If you are unable to find it when you return, simply go away again and come back when it has got dark.

M. Ross
Stockwell

DON'T buy expensive 'ribbed' condoms. Just use an ordinary one, and slip a handful of frozen peas inside before putting it on.

D. Duckham
Didford

MIX petrol with stuffing and roll it in the palm of your hands to make handy sized 'petrol balls'.

B. Baxter
Potters Bar

WHEN carrying a cup of tea from one room to another always add a desert spoon of cornflour. This will thicken it up and prevent it from spilling on the carpet.

Mrs E. Davis
Blackpool

HOUSE guests will think your fingernails grow very quickly if you cut up a table tennis ball, and scatter small pieces around your bathroom sink every morning.

F. Foster
Froddingham

MOTORISTS. When parking in car parks always carry a spare battery in the boot in case your other one has gone flat by the time you return to the car.

M. Ross
Stockwell

BRITAIN'S BARBERS FACE THE CHOP

Britain's much heralded entry into Europe in 1992 has spelled disaster for the British barber. For Euro hair trends have lead to a dramatic drop in business.

OUT have gone the traditional short back and sides, pudding bowl and basin cuts – the staple business of the British barber.

IN has come the Euro hair do – long, girly hair, with a little beard, and leather pants (like Bjorn out of Abba).

LOCKS

And the new craze for lengthier locks has meant a lot less business for hairdressers.

- **SNIP!** Visits to the hairdressers are down by over 50 per cent on 1991 figures.
- **SNIP!** A lot less hair is being cut off, with the length of haircuts down by a staggering 75 per cent.
- **SNIP!** Four out of ten High Street barbers shops will go bust by the end of the year.

TOE PATHS

As one barber told us, things are desperate. "I've never known things this bad in all the years I've been a barber. People simply aren't coming in, and if they do they only want a few pence worth of hair cutting off."

A typical 'European' haircut (above) which is bad news for barbers like this one (below).

But while the European look reeks havoc for gents' hairdressers, ladies' stylists are doing big business. For the trendy continental cut for girls is the short, 'lesbian' style haircut, and cash registers are ringing in ladies' salons throughout the UK.

20 THINGS YOU NEVER KNEW ABOUT SHOES

An attractive shoe model displays the very latest fashion in footwear - shoes.

Fred Astaire danced in them, footballers score goals with them. Everybody wears them, from the Queen all the way down to Jeremy Beadle. Yes, love them or hate them SHOES are here to stay. But how many facts do you know about footwear? Here are twenty things you probably never knew about the shoe.

1 There's nothing new about the shoe. They've been around for a lot longer than you'd think. In cave men days dinosaur skin shoes – with flint soles – were all the rage. Stone age cobblers would charge around 6 dinosaur teeth (about £22.99 in today's money) for a pair, complete with thick black curly laces – made out of mammoth pubes.

2 Say "shoe" to a dog and it won't scurry off to fetch your footwear. It will simply run away. That's because the word "shoe" in dog language means "clear off".

3 However, if you say "fetch" to the same dog, after it's come back, it may then go off and get your slippers – special soft indoor shoes made out of checky cloth.

4 If you find a shoe tree in your garden, don't climb up it hoping to pick shoes. For a shoe tree isn't a tree at all. We think it's something to do with shoes that you sometimes find in the bottom of wardrobes – possibly for putting inside shoes. A bit like a mug tree, but for shoes, not mugs.

A normal tree yesterday

5 However, some shoes *do* grow on trees. For in Holland drug-crazed Netherlanders hobble about their windmills in clumsy wooden 'clogs'. These traditional, impractical and uncomfortable shoes were originally worn to protect Dutch feet from flooding dykes, and have since been adopted as part of the national costume.

6 The smallest shoes ever made were a pair of clogs presented by King Van der Vaalk VI of Netherland to the world's smallest man, Kalvin Phillips of Bridgewater, USA. The tiny shoes, an incredible size .00008 (European size 41) were carved from the two halves of a single salted peanut. However, Dutch microcobblers over did it – and the clogs were fractionally too small for 8 inch tall Phillips, who complained that they nipped his toes. Ironically, Phillips died shortly afterwards, and was buried – in a shoebox!

7 Nowadays shoes are made from many different materials. For example, Cinderella, in the pantomime of the same name, went to the ball wearing glass slippers.

8 And in the nursery rhyme of the same name, an old lady who *lived* in a shoe had so many children she didn't know what to do.

9 So she gave them some broth without any bread.

10 And spanked them all soundly and sent them to bed. The rotten cow.

11 Ask a musician if he plays the shoe horn and the chances are he'll give you a blank stare. That's because a shoe horn is, in fact, a machine, often found in hotel corridors, to enable you to put your shoes on quickly.

12 Buy a pair of shoes nowadays and you can bet that an embarrassed spotty teenage shop assistant will half-heartedly try to sell you some cheap shoe polish. That's because shoe shop managers only pay their staff 25p an hour, and then offer them a commission on sales of crap shoe polish.

13 The world's best-selling shoe has sold over 100 million pairs since it was invented by a victorian chiropodist in 1887. Dr Jeremiah Marten noticed the barefoot street urchins in his home town of Northampton developed sore toes from kicking each other in the head. So he set about inventing his patented leather 'aggro boot', and the Doctor Marten was born.

Dr Jeremiah Marten - 'aggro boot'

14 At about the same time in Sweden Dr Jergen Schol, a humble carpenter, made his wife a pair of dangerous and uncomfortable flat shoes or 'sandals' by nailing the cuffs from an old shirt onto two short lengths of splintered floor-board. His popular sandals are still worn today by librarians and medical receptionists, and can be bought at car boot sales for around 10p.

Dr Hugo White did not invent any shoes. He invented jam rags.

16 There are many kinds of boots. Walking boots, climbing boots, football boots, cowboy boots and Boots the Chemists, a large pharmaceutical manufacturer and retailer based in Nottingham.

17 There are also car boots, but if you try one on for size you'll probably find that it's a little roomy. That's because a car boot is the space at the back of your car where you put your suitcases.

18 But don't turn up at a car boot sale expecting to buy a new boot for your car. Car boot sales are special sales held in car parks where you can buy a 1970's lava lamp – guaranteed to blow up and burn your house down – for only 75p. (But they'll take fifty. Oh, go on then. Twenty-five).

19 They say that horse shoes bring good luck. But horses themselves would probably disagree. That's because a horse shoe is just a great big Blakey's seg nailed onto the horses toes.

A horse three weeks ago

20 They also say that an army marches on its stomach, but any soldier will tell you that's nonsense. For they march in Wellington boots, so named after the Grand Old Duke of York who invented the Cardigan Jumper at the Battle of Balaclava in 1066, etc. etc. etc.

HERE IT IS!
Welcome to the first annual

Viz *postal* SUMMER

Welcome one and all to Fulchester village green for the first annual Viz summer fete. And what smashing weather we've got for it! Sunshine is guaranteed all day long for this special *postal* fete, the proceeds of which will go towards Fulchester parish church's steeple restoration fund. There's something for everyone. Fun and games, tea and cakes, competitions, exhibitions, prizes, raffles – there's even a display of dog handling by a local police constable.

In order to enhance your enjoyment of this Summer Fete, why not try reading these pages in the garden while the sun is shining.

GRAND OPENING
by TV's 'Lively Lad'
RODNEY BEWES

> I NOW DECLARE THIS FETE OPEN

★ ★ ★ ★ ★ ★ ★ ★ ★ ★ ★ ★ ★ ★ ★ ★ ★

OLD MRS THOMPSON'S
WHITE ELEPHANT STALL

Take your pick from the various items of bric-a-brac on display. If anything takes your fancy, look up the price in the table below, and send your money to Old Mrs Thompson's White Elephant stall (see address at end). Mrs Thompson reserves the right to send you a different item if the one you want is already sold.

Books - 5p Records - 10p Rice painting - 35p
Table tennis net (some parts missing) - 5p Paint - 10p
Lampshade - 20p, Umbrella - 20p, Clock 15p
Flowerpots - 5p (2 for 8p) Space gun (broken) 10p
Toilet freshener 6p, Computer stick 20p (electric)

GIANT FRUIT AND VEGETABLE COMPETITION

To be judged by Mr Collins the grocer. Do **YOU** have an unusually large fruit or vegetable? Perhaps you've grown a big grapefruit, or cultivated a large carrot. Or maybe you just bought a funny shaped potato or something. Send your entries to Mr Collins, who regrets that no fruit or veg can be returned. The winner will receive a rosette and a voucher worth £5 valid at Mr Collin's shop on Fulchester High Street.

DOG HANDLING DISPLAY by P.